A DARKNESS
LIT BY HEROES

A DARKNESS
LIT BY HEROES

The Granite Mountain-Speculator
Mine Disaster of 1917
Butte, Montana

DOUG AMMONS

Water Nymph Press
Missoula, Montana

Bill —
Glad you found the show
of interest & as fascinating
as I do. Best,
Doug

Copyright © 2017 Doug Ammons

Source for drawings on pages 71; 170 (Schematic layout of the Granite Mountain and Speculator Shafts; LaMartine's Route exploring the 2200): *Harrington, D. (1922)* Lessons of from the Granite Mountain Shaft Fire, Butte, *Bureau of Mines – Dept. of Interior, Figure 2, page 11; Plate II, page 55.*

Source for map page 151 –ACM map of the Butte Hill. Original adapted by permission from Butte-Silver Bow Archives
All other maps based on drawings by Doug Ammons

Cover and Back Cover by S. R. Walker Designs, Budford, GA
Original Artwork by Kim Abney, Knoxville, TN
Photograph of Tom LaMartine and text, page 1, *Anaconda Standard* June 12, 1917
Photograph of page 1, the *Anaconda Standard*, June 12, 1917
Covers: Mining maps courtesy of Butte-Silver Bow Archives, Butte, Montana

FRONT COVER:
  TOP: Granite Mountain headframe in snow. Photo by Doug Ammons, 2014.
  RIGHT SIDE: A section of the 2400 workings of the Edith May vein, the far western part of the Speculator mine. Ernest Sullau ran through these tunnels to warn miners after accidently lighting the fire in the Granite Mountain shaft.

BACK COVER:
The 2439C drift, part of the Snowball vein area (the "C" switch, 2403C and connected workings) in the far eastern part of the Speculator mine, where Manus Duggan died trying to escape to the Rainbow shaft.

Library of Congress Cataloging-in-Publication Data

Ammons, Doug
A Darkness Lit by Heroes: The Granite Mountain-Speculator Mine Disaster of 1917/Doug Ammons-1st Ed.
252 Pages 19 Figures
ISBN 978-0-692-90042-0
1. Speculator-Granite Mountain Mine 2. Mine disaster 3. Butte Montana 4. Human Drama 5. History

Printing by Quad Graphics, Michigan

First Edition

Water Nymph Press
Missoula, MT
www.dougammons.com

Dedicated to the people of Butte, Montana

and

To William F. "Duke" Crowley and Matthew F. Canning

LIST OF CHAPTERS

PREFACE

The Speculator Mine fire of 1917 was the biggest hard rock mining disaster and one of the most heart-rending events in the history of America. One hundred and sixty eight men died, two hundred and forty lived. This book was written to reveal the experience of the miners and their families, struggling to survive when suddenly thrust into life and death situations and forces beyond their control.

It is a story of what men do when they are stripped to the core. We see every reaction a human is capable of, from blind animal panic to the most inspiring and courageous self-sacrifice. The goal of the book was to pull readers underground, directly into the chaos, heartache, and courage as experienced by the men and their families. Through this, we see a reflection of ourselves. The outer story is about a mining disaster; the real story is about the strength of the human spirit.

The primary details and most of the smaller particulars are from the historical record. This book is essentially a documentary, but presented in the form of a novel rather than a journalistic report. The information came from multiple sources: dozens of newspaper articles during and after the disaster from the *Butte Miner, Anaconda Standard,* and *Butte Daily Post.* They also include the official federal report for the Bureau of Mines by Daniel Harrington (*Lessons of the Granite Mountain Fire,* 1922), and private correspondence of various miners held by the Butte-Silver Bow Archives. The largest source was the six hundred pages of eye-witness testimony from the coroner's inquest, held in Butte the summer of 1917. More than seventy miners testified, including members of all the groups of men who are presented in the book.

Additionally, over one hundred formerly proprietary maps of the Speculator and adjacent mines were found and closely analyzed. Great effort was made to match the men's testimony with the specific drifts, stopes, and manways they referred to, making it possible to identify where they worked and how they attempted to escape. This included essentially all the positions,

1

movements, and routes of the men, which also helped recreate their decision-making.

The collected papers of the North Butte Mining Company, held in Helena at the Montana Historical Society, were consulted closely. Weekly and monthly correspondence between the Speculator mine's manager, Norman Braly, and the New York and Minnesota offices of the company, were used to identify concerns about equipment and production, orders, mining strategies for the different veins, and specific active areas in the weeks before the disaster. This was used to create descriptions of the ongoing work just prior to the disaster, what foreman Ernest Sullau and the shift bosses under him were told, and what they knew. The mine was the largest, deepest, and most complex in the world at that time.

After the fire started, pulses of smoke and gas chased the men throughout this vast underground. Their movements were reconstructed using maps of the tunnels, connecting vertical manways, distances, and interpreting the physical and engineering reasons for the paths they took, and where the smoke and gas went. The latter is a difficult task, as there were hundreds of miles of tunnels, four ventilation shafts, and temperature differences more than seventy degrees from the surface to the 3000 foot level.

A detailed time-line was created for the main characters and some minor characters, locating them by place and action throughout the mine as the disaster unfolded. Every effort was made to tell the story accurately from inside the men's experience. Three Butte mining engineers helped interpret details.

This approach revealed many unknown aspects of the disaster, as well as additional details of well-established stories, such as what happened to the tragic heroes Ernest Sullau, Manus Duggan, and JD Moore. Further, it allowed recreating remarkable action sequences and insight into the decisions made by the men. Other fascinating substories appeared as well.

Most of the men were blunt. They did not reveal their feelings, some could hardly speak English, and all used mining slang with poor grammar. When reading the coroner's inquest, if one does not know the terms, tasks, or the layout of the mine, much of the testimony is impossible to understand in any detail.

Also, there are contradictions across men and even within the same individuals at different points in their testimony. In every such case, helped by consulting the Butte mining engineers, the best interpretation was made.

Raw quotes, phrases, wording, and direct descriptions of situations and conversations were taken from the inquest or other sources. Other dialogue, text, and the men's internal thoughts were constructed from immediate implications of their statements, or the dilemmas and choices, as determined from the situations, informed by the maps, the equipment, the standard tasks and knowledge of the men's jobs.

One important note: it is impossible to determine every fact. For example, the last name of Stanley Laszkeics, the Polish-Russian immigrant who bulkheaded with JD Moore, is spelled nine different ways in the historical sources. Many details in the story have similar discrepancies, including comments and statements by the men. When multiple sources are compared, they generally line up, but some conflict. In the end, the researcher must make a decision and readers must realize that history, no matter how many sources there are, is not absolute. It is a product of the historian, the story told, sources, unconscious sympathies, style of writing, and who edits. Above all, it reflects the fact that human experience is malleable. The lived experience happens precisely once ever, and the people who are present see different things. Even the same person remembers it differently as time goes on. I have done my best to make this story tightly describe the original event, as it happened, in the most intimate way possible.

I would like to thank certain people for their help, without which this book could not have been written.

Ellen Crain and the wonderful ladies at the Butte-Silver Bow Archives provided constant support and willingness to ferret out virtually any kind of information about Butte. With Ellen, are Irene, Nikole, Aubrey, Harriett, and Kim in particular. They are responsible for handing me the six hundred pages of the inquest and its fascinating testimony, which set the whole project in motion. The archives house a treasure trove of materials. With their able help, people can time-travel back into Butte's history and capture glimpses of what likely was the wildest city on the face of the earth.

I owe a great deal to the generous help of three Butte mining engineers, Floyd Bossard, Larry Hoffman, and Dave Kneebone, drawing from their more than one hundred and fifty years of collective experience underground. All interpretations were discussed with them, and their personal experiences were incorporated into many descriptions. They were patient in answering questions and talking about hundreds of topics in mining engineering and technology specific to the history of Butte's mines, examining detailed passages from the inquest, and the specific situations in the Speculator disaster. Discussions with all of them ranged widely into the human side of mining and helped me enter the minds of the men.

I am grateful to Floyd for in-depth discussions about the disaster and specific interpretations of how the North Butte Mining Company engineered their ventilation system and responded to the underground fire. For decades he was one of the world's experts in mine ventilation. He became a good friend, but unfortunately passed away as this book was entering its final stages. I am sorry that he was not able to see how his thinking influenced the content. Larry was an inexhaustible treasure trove of practical mining experience and equally knowledgeable about mining history. Even after spending a lifetime mining, he remains deeply curious and fascinated with all aspects of technology and human problem-solving, both above and below ground. Dave's huge knowledge of mine safety was instrumental for certain descriptions of the inner workings of the mine, and the reactions and thought processes of rescuers. While Floyd has passed, I hope to continue enjoying my friendships with Larry and Dave. It will be obvious to them how they changed my perspective, and how their professional and personal interpretations were used.

Many thanks to Ted Duaime for providing a number of maps which helped me see the physical relationships inside the Speculator and surrounding mines. To Tom Malloy, with whom I hope to spend many another afternoon inside old Butte mineyards and under the headframes. To Pat Riordan, who ably created maps using GIS data that helped my understanding of the hill. To Jeannette Kopf at the World Museum of Mining for permission sleuthing through photographs, and Dan Peters who gave me a number of interesting anecdotes. To Tommy Holter and Lou Loushin for colorful descriptions of mining, cables, and operating the mines' giant hoist engines. To Michael Punke, who carefully used historical documents and personal interviews to write his book, *Fire and Brimstone*.

Gerry and Fred Walters are gratefully acknowledged, without their care and determination the Granite Mountain Memorial would not have its powerful presence at the top of the Butte Hill. Mark Reavis, Butte's long-time Historical Preservation Officer and licensed architect, designed the memorial and chose its somber location, hallowed ground that overlooks the Granite Mountain headframe and remnants of the Speculator mineyard. Mark additionally provided me with many insights into Butte, as did Richard Gibson and Jim Street, both of whom kindly shared historical documents. Matt Krattiger had excellent suggestions.

Thanks to Stephen Walker for the cover design, and to Kim Abney, who did the three-dimensional depictions of the tunnels in the mine and other illustrations. Ruth Dant of Quad Graphics was essential to printing the book.

My wife Robin deserves special thanks. She was with me every step of the way with suggestions, prodding, and demanding excellence as she edited my one thousand pages down to a measly two hundred. My mother Dr. Carol Ammons was a constant encouragement, editor, and enthusiastic contributor to the book.

Finally, I would like to thank William F. "Duke" Crowley, a native of Walkerville and a self-described street kid of Butte, who started Robin's and my journey into Silver Bow County. Duke was our neighbor for more than thirty years and generously described Butte to us through his eyes. I hope this book will do that for others. I thank Duke's father William Crowley, who was a helmet man in the disaster. Also, Duke's grandfather, Matthew Canning, who remains an inspiration and an impressive man, showing how immigrants to America and Butte in 1900 contributed so much to this country.

INTRODUCTION

And the LORD God formed man of the dust of the ground...
Genesis 2:7

At the height of the Rocky Mountains was a valley nestled against the Great Divide. There the wind rolled dry, pressing over the sagebrush and colorless grass. The north end of the valley climbed upward, cut by shallow gullies, to the top of a hill. From there one could see the surrounding peaks, snow-clad even in summer, and to the east was the jagged wall of the Divide.

Out on the flats, two creeks curled and wound. Fed by springs, one ran from a canyon in the north and the other from the forested foothills in the south. Close to the hill they met and formed a meandering course of silver bows, lined by willow trees. A narrow lushness that curved through the dry expanse, fed from the crown of the continent.

In the 1860s men came to the valley to placer mine. Eager for gold dust, they shoveled the sand out of the silver bows and into rocker boxes, working alone, pouring their strength into their shovels. For a few, the energy they put in equaled the gold they brought out. But that was the exception, for most squandered their life energy into nothing but piles of barren gravel.

When the gold dust was gone in the creeks, other men pursued the dry gullies of the hill, but the gold did not last any longer there.

Lore has it that on the hill, an unknown miner noticed the colored streaks in the granite outcrops and began to dig. His placer claims must have played out, but his dreams had not. On the lonely hillside, enticed by glittering crystals, he scraped a small trench into a quartz vein with a worn and chipped antler, prying small pieces loose. Iron pyrite crystals, fool's gold.

What he did not know was that there were mineral veins below him running a mile deep into the hill, and they hid more riches than his wildest dreams or his antler could ever reach. The first steel picks and shovels painstakingly worked a few feet into the ground. Soon, they went further.

In 1875 they dug hundreds of feet deeper seeking silver. By the early 1880s Edison invented the light-bulb and Bell the telephone, and some men saw the future. Suddenly the world wanted copper, and they found it in Butte.

To understand the hill, one has to know the minerals. A granite batholith formed the eighty mile length of the mountains along the Divide. Molten rock welled up from inside the earth, rising close to the surface. As it neared its zenith, it began to cool and break. Giant cracks appeared throughout it. Under huge pressures, the last melted quartz and scalding water injected into the cracks, filled with precious metals. The mixture cooled into veins and bodies of ore that contained the richest copper deposit in the world.

Lone prospectors evolved into miners and engineers, geologists and metallurgists. The antler evolved into dynamite and compressed air drills, and into giant hoisting machines. Placer mining in the soft sands of Silver Bow Creek turned into deep mines through solid rock.

By 1900, there was a crowd of millionaires, but only three men reigned as kings, Marcus Daly, William A. Clark, and Fritz Augustus Heinze. By that time, Butte was no longer a rag tag of prospectors weighing gold dust, it was a place to get a job, and the mines were the best paying in the world. They required huge numbers of workers, with jobs from backbreaking unskilled labor to dozens of new specialized skills. In turn, these men built a city that could sustain them, one that reflected every dream, virtue, and vice they had. And as its reputation grew, people came from every corner of the world, their dreams were the raw clay from which it was made.

But the Copper Kings did not last forever and the wealth attracted other eyes. After 1900, Daly was gone, his mines sold out to a consortium of hard-nosed Wall Street investors who set in motion plans to control the world's copper market. Under their flagship holding company, Amalgamated Copper, they expected a quick conquest.

They did not plan on being outsmarted by the youngest copper king, the pirate F. A. Heinze, who at first appeared totally outgunned. It was a battle of seven years, Heinze's bold and reckless stratagems against their financial power and ruthlessness. He was a brigand and a brilliant geologist, finding rich ore on claims where there supposedly was none, and deftly steering a stable of thirty-five lawyers against Amalgamated. He outraged the financial behemoth, pulled the teeth of their ruthlessness, and raided their underground ore. Law suits and politics above ground, secret tunnels, grenades, fists, and slaked lime below. He finally sold out to them in 1906 for the equivalent of nearly a billion dollars.

By 1910, shadows of the copper kings still were there, their names stamped upon the city and state, but a new wave had started. Amalgamated, reincarnated into the Anaconda Company, ruled most of the hill, but not all. Clark continued quietly and no longer in the forefront.

Into the upheaval left by Heinze's departure stepped the North Butte Mining Company, run by a small group of canny investors. They hired excellent geologists and mining engineers, and purchased the best equipment. To the surprise of old timers, they bought the Speculator mine, known for its cave-ins and sweltering heat. Inexplicably, they bought the Granite Mountain claim, which was mostly barren rock. Then they strategically acquired a swath of old claims from the top of the hill down the east side. The holdings combined more than fifteen small mines, the Edith May, Adirondack, Jessie, Gem, and others, into one large mine with access to nine major ore veins. Then the company sank the Granite Mountain shaft and from it, drove crosscuts out across all the veins, making them highways that united dozens of drifts on each level.

They were not copper kings, but it was the North Butte's genius to realize they could expand the Speculator into a lucrative holding of a kind no copper king envisioned, a single monolithic mine. It quickly became the biggest and deepest mine on the richest hill in the world. With new methods and technology there was as much wealth as ever.

The deeper they went, the more powerful the machines needed, and none was more essential than the hoist. In 1917, the biggest was the four thousand horsepower electric hoist at the

9

Granite Mountain shaft. The hoist was the lifeline between the miners underground and the surface, and the shaft was the path by which everything was lifted and lowered in the mine. It was the only direct way in or out – the key link of a complex system that allowed mining deep in the earth.

The Granite Mountain hoist was perhaps the most powerful electric engine that had ever been built. From a dead stop, the hoist was rated for sixty thousand pounds. It could lift that weight at almost forty miles an hour, twice as fast as any other hoist. Ten tons of ore, eight tons for the metal skip that held the ore, and ten tons of steel cable down into the shaft, plus all the frictional losses involved. The instantaneous starting horsepower was infinite. The stresses on the headframe, engine, and the drum were far beyond anything ever handled before. All the power was strung on a steel cable connecting the hoist engine at the surface to the loaded skips thousands of feet underground.

Stepping through the door of the engine room, one was immersed in a deep hum. The new high voltage transmission lines came from the Hauser, Madison, and Canyon Ferry dams, driving a large motor and the main electrical generator, which spun up an eighty-six ton flywheel. It was twelve feet across, made of steel a foot and a half thick, and its outer rim rotated at two hundred and fifty miles an hour, ready to throw its enormous power into the hoist's loads.

When the hoist engineer engaged the motor to lift a ten-ton ore skip, the motor drew a huge pulse of current. Early on, it could steal all the current in the transmission lines, blacking out lights from Butte to the hydro-generators at the Canyon Ferry dam more than eighty miles away. The pulses instantly melted any wires unable to handle the load.

The steel flywheel solved the blackouts and meltdowns. When the hoist motor engaged one of the enormous ore skips, the inertia of the spinning flywheel provided the peaking force, surging current into the voracious motor. With the flywheel behind it, the hoist could pull through anything.

The air of the engine room was thick with the vibration of huge power coiled. The hoist engineer wielded that power through the palms of his hands, resting on the steel levers, enough power to wreck the shaft, or tear apart the headframe, to pull an ore skip through the top and crush an idler tower. Enough to kill forty men if he made a mistake when a shift was being lifted, or effortlessly cut a man in half if the cage was not clear.

The engine room was his domain. His eyes scanned every detail and what it told him about the hoist, the engine and shaft, the skips and cages. The cable spooled off the twelve-foot drums and out the window toward the headframe, and he listened to the sing of its tension and the hum of the engine, making sure the tone stayed even when the drums spun at speed, ready to throw on the brakes if the motor lugged down.

Back and forth for the entire shift he released clutches and engaged the motor as the counterbalanced skips worked up and down thousands of feet of shaft. He could guide an unseen cage three thousand feet below in the shaft, a half-mile away from him, and stop its floor against the turnsheets of the station to within half an inch. There had never been a combination of power, skill, and precision like it.

Nobody bothered the engineer when the hoist was in use, he listened only to the signal bells. Coded rings were the language the skip tenders used to tell him where to take a load, to lift, or to lower.

And most of all, to tell him "all clear."

CHAPTER ONE

MEN OF THE SPECULATOR

In the west-side neighborhoods, north of Park Street and south of the Anselmo mine, four of the Speculator mine's night shift bosses lived within two blocks of each other – JD Moore at 426 North Alabama, John Collins a block down, Jack Bronson on Caledonia, and Albert Weigenstein on Edison.

Six days a week, they went to work together at four-thirty on the city trolley, catching it on Park and going through the teeming streets and high rise buildings of Uptown. They made the connection onto Anaconda Road into the dense Irish neighborhood of Dublin Gulch and got off to walk the final leg past the High Ore mine.

Gruff and taciturn, they knew how rock, dynamite, and men worked. They were handy with their calloused hands, whether on a shovel, drill, or timbering a stope. The shift bosses were handy with their fists too, if orders failed and they needed to make a point. Telling hard men what to do was their business. If they did not know their job, they did not last long. But the deal was simple, they themselves worked even harder and wanted the best for their men.

The hill had scores of angular steel frames jutting up, each with a waste dump and compressor plant spewing smoke. Railroad tracks crisscrossed slopes and led into spurs beside high bins. Along a web of paths and roads walked fifteen thousand working men every day, drillers to muckers, geologists to station tenders, and fifty other jobs that pulled ore out of the ground and spread copper around the world.

Men worked for money and a job, but deep underground the honesty of the shared danger was their bond. There was no lying to the rock, the dynamite, or to each other. These bonds were brought up into the city and made a community as tight as a band of brothers.

Every kind of man lived in Butte, casual and rakish to quiet and serious, but those who were scared did not last long. There were men who spoke no English and were on their first shifts. Swarthy sawed-off Greek men, young fair-haired Irish boys, thick-boned Finns, and feisty Cornish Cousin Jacks.

***

On the top of the hill at five o'clock in the afternoon, Stanley Laszkeics laced up his work boots and prepared to head to the mine. Theirs was one of ten small houses lining the short length of Clark Street in the densely populated gullies of Walkerville. Right above them to the north was the old Alice mine, while the Lexington loomed above them just to the south, black steel silhouette like the ramparts of an ocean vessel against the moving sky. Over the ridge to the east was the Speculator where he worked.

He grabbed one of the soft warm rolls cooling on the top of the stove and spread butter on it, catching the melted drips with his finger and spreading them back onto the bread. His wife Helen had packed his dinner, a large tin pot of thick ham hock stew and fresh rolls.

He loved the taste from the Old Country, but more importantly, he felt for the weight of the bucket, checking whether there was enough to see him through the shift. The hard labor required every ounce of food he could swallow, and if there were any leftovers, they were eaten quickly when his children rifled through his lunch bucket the next morning, looking for treasured pieces of cookies or cakes.

Helen ran the household, always with a child in her arms. She was dedicated to her husband, a quiet, hard-working man who rarely shared his thoughts, but loved her and the children. Although life was hard, she was happy with Stanley.

Their four-year old son Clements played next to the dirt road outside, muddy-fingered in a puddle. The twins had just finished their nap and were talking a polyglot of Russian and Polish, with a scattering of English the way that children do when brought up by immigrant parents. The two oldest daughters, Stella and Helen, named for her mother, had been gathering coal from along the railroad tracks just up the hill. Their darting eyes watched for the loaded train to the Lexington mine's compressor plant, broken shards and pieces of coal falling from its cars as it rumbled past, and they came back with a small gunny sack half-full for heating that night.

"Come on, Stella!" shouted Helen, "Papa leaves soon!" as they hurried to be in time to say goodbye to their father.

Stanley smiled when he saw them come down the road, carrying the sack between them, and took the coal in one hand and with the other, pulled them close in their smudged hand-me-down dresses.

Stanley was in his late thirties, born in Polish Russia in 1880, and arrived in the United States a decade before. He became a miner in West Virginia, then heard of the mines of Michigan and Idaho. Word-of-mouth led him farther, stories of new and better jobs in Butte, and he arrived with his family in tow. With the wages, he bought a small house. Three children quickly became six.

He left his house promptly at ten after five, or at least tried to. Every day the children invented demands to keep him and his warm laugh close. Clements wanted to be picked up. The twins clamored for a last hug. Stella watched, standing in line for a kiss on the cheek before skipping off.

Stanley finally unwrapped himself from all the little arms and headed to the Spec. His oldest daughter Helen, a wide-eyed, slender girl all of six years old, liked to walk with him part way, holding two fingers of his hand, savoring its rough but loving touch until the first bend of the road.

There she stood and watched him until he reached the crest of the ridge. She could see his small figure next to the Corra headframe, waving to her, and she waved back, whispering softly "Goodbye, Father," in Polish, *Do widzenia Tato.*"

Then he crossed over to the other side and was gone.

***

Manus Duggan came to Butte from Pennsylvania looking for work, part of the constant stream of young hungry men from around the country and overseas. For eight years he lived in the Brogan's boarding house and worked at the Speculator. He appreciated their neatly packed lunches, heaping dinners, and a hot shower after the night shift. Brogan's was small compared to the unruly packed houses on the east side, places like the Big Ship with 400 men, or those for a dollar a week where three men, one from the day, night, and maintenance shifts, would share a single room and bed, each sleeping his allotted hours on the mattress cast over a flimsy bed frame, then grabbing his clothes and leaving to make way for the next man. Those were not living spaces, but berths for sleeping, and the rest of the time the men worked their shift, or frequented the saloons and brothels while each of the room-mates slept in turn. A single bulb hanging, a dresser shoved against the wall, boots in the corner, a few letters stuffed in a drawer.

The worst places were not boarding houses, but shanties in the off streets with fifteen unkempt men sleeping on the floor. Utility ruled. Butte crammed in over one thousand people per block and there was reason for escape and any pleasure was seized. The city teemed with restless men who worked, drank, and gambled, packing themselves into the two hundred and fifty saloons twenty-four hours a day.

Brogan's boarding house was run by a fine Irish woman, Mary Brogan, a woman of boundless hospitality who cooked, cleaned, and exacted manners from her boarders. She demanded more than rent; it was her home, there were customs and rules. Manus appreciated there were no doors swinging open in the middle of the night, no loud yelling or drunkenness, regardless of what the men were accustomed to on the streets.

Mary's daughter, Madge, grew up among the boarders and had a keen eye. Manus' quiet confidence and shy smile attracted her, and she decided early that he was the man she wanted. *The finest man I ever saw*, she thought to herself. He had a steady job and worked as a nipper in the Speculator, carrying sharpened drill bits and other tools to drilling crews. They married in 1915. With

15

his savings, he built her a home at 1010 Zarelda Street up on the west side, complete with an inside toilet.

To get to work, Duggan had the choice to take the trolley up around through Walkerville and walk over the ridge to the Speculator, or take the trolley across on Park Street through Uptown and Dublin Gulch. He varied it, the same way he enjoyed the variety of his nipper job, never being tied to a particular route underground.

Manus stood in the front room about to leave, and reached out, gently running his hand over Madge's round belly. She took his hand and clasped it in hers, pressing it into the baby inside her. He leaned into her saying quietly, "You're going to be a mother soon."

She looked up and rested her head on his shoulder, "I wish I felt better right now."

"Should I stay home and help you?"

"No, go to work, I'll be fine."

He smiled at her changing form and how the hem of her dress hiked up in front. "Take care of your mama, Little Oscar," he said quietly.

"You'll be surprised if it's a girl, with your eyes."

He brushed back her hair and let his hand gently slide down and linger on her cheek. She held his gaze for a few moments, and he bent down. His arm encircled her and he moved his hand down the curve of her back and pulled her close. Seconds were drawn out, and in the quiet of the house she felt his strength, even and sure.

Manus stepped slowly toward the door, squeezing past her, his lips on hers. The kiss broke and she saw his boyish smile, "Time for work," he said, and quickly walked up to the street.

Madge stood on the porch and watched him walk toward the trolley stop on Excelsior. After a block, he turned around and waved as she was looking, and she waved again. The car appeared and he swung himself up, light on his feet. She could see his hand through the window and a glimpse of him, then the trolley moved down the hill out of sight.

16

Joe Barnicoat lived on Park Street several blocks into the west side of Butte, away from the noise of the mines and dark fumes of the smelters. The streets rolled up and down the gulches, houses packed in with family bakeries and grocery stores. Further west beyond his house were the streets of high society, lined with the mansions of mine owners and bankers, until the city graded back into working class neighborhoods near the Anselmo mine.

Barnicoat had moved to Butte in 1909, finding a job at the Speculator just as they started sinking the new Granite Mountain shaft. He was hired as the topman, gatekeeper of all activity in and out of the shaft. Under the headframe he secured loads of dynamite, drills, and timber, directed hundreds of workers on and off cages, and signaled bells for every destination underground. Every shift change, he oversaw the loading and unloading until the entire shift had been lowered to their working places somewhere in three hundred miles of tunnels honeycombing the rock.

Men went where they were told. When needed, Barnicoat was firm enough to make willful men listen and curse a wagon that got too close to the shaft. "Watch the collar!" He knew every bit of scuttlebutt in the mine and joked with the shift bosses and contract miners. Everyone on the night shift knew and respected him.

Hard rock mining was perfected in Cornwall, the far southwest peninsula of Great Britain that his family called home. For generations, the men mined the tin and copper deposits of the Cornish batholith, and he was not going to change their tradition.

His neighbor was Matt Canning, whose birthplace was across the Celtic Sea from Barnicoat's, an Irishman from the poor, rocky northwest of the Emerald Isle. County Mayo was hit hardest by the famine, creating orphans, overcrowded workhouses, and an outpouring of immigrants seeking new lives around the world. As the saying went, "You're from County Mayo? God save you."

Matt was schooled as a seminarian near Dublin, but instead of the priesthood, he ran away to Butte at twenty-two with a young lassie who became his wife. He took work as a miner, when drilling was by hand and light was by candle. But from his years in

17

the seminary he had a fine education, and so he studied law at night, got an office Uptown, and wrestled this wild-west city filled with brothels and saloons, where the cops were always five bar fights behind.

Canning was well-muscled from his years working underground, and still looked more like a miner than a lawyer. He struck an imposing figure, broad-shouldered, keen-eyed, with the top of his fedora a foot taller than Barnicoat's cap.

Barnicoat and Canning had sons the same age, but unfortunately, Canning's wife had suddenly passed away. He relied on his oldest daughter Linda to help raise a house full of children, and if needed, Mrs. Barnicoat next door set Canning's household to order as well as her own.

Heading to work in the late afternoon, Barnicoat stepped out of his house at 606 West Park and saw Canning briskly walking home along the cobblestone street, hefting a briefcase in one hand, and chewing a cigar under his black moustache. Canning offered his free hand and a smile, "Joe, how's your work going?"

"She's good, mine's 3700 feet to the bottom now," answered Barnicoat.

Canning took the cigar out of his lips, "I remember working at a thousand feet, swinging a sledge. We thought we were deep then."

"When you look up that shaft, ain't a spot of daylight to be seen," Barnicoat smiled. "I saw a map of the workings in manager Braly's office. We're the biggest mine there is," he said with satisfaction.

The trolley came up the hill from the west side, ringing its bell. "That's my ride."

"Catch me up sometime!" Canning called after him. His friend jumped up on the car, gave a wave, and was off.

***

Ernest Sullau was the night foreman for the Speculator mine. With his wife he lived on Wall Street out on the flats, right

18

on a main trolley route. From the back porch of their house one could see the hill covered with black headframes, poking up like giant ship masts captured on land. Every change of shift, a chorus of steam whistles blew from the mineyards and started the exodus of tired workers out of the mines, and an army of men from the city down into the mines.

His reputation was for hard work and terse, well-aimed words, but most of all he was known for his strength. His body was thick and his hands were massive, like anvils. Early in his career, he drilled dynamite holes with a four-pound hammer in one steel grip and a chiseled bit in the other. He could set a twelve-by-twelve timber by himself. From mucker to miner, then to boss, he helped build the crosscuts and drifts, level by level, stope by stope, drilling, blasting, and timbering. More than any other individual man, his hands had made the Speculator mine. When they were looking to replace the night foreman, he was the easy choice.

Born in Hamburg, Germany, Sullau had arrived in Butte seventeen years before. Fifteen of those years he worked at the Speculator as it grew from the smallest claim to the most complex and deepest mine on the hill, climbing his way up job by job with every tool he learned to use, shovels and picks, hammers and drills, pushing ore cars and laying rails.

His years of effort inscribed a tactile map of the working mine. He knew every crew, motorman, and station from the surface down; the manways and ladder systems, floors and levels, all were a part of him, giving him a visceral feel of the Speculator's underground.

Sullau became a miner in Butte when the Copper Kings still fought among themselves, and he watched with dubious curiosity when the North Butte Company bought the Spec in 1905. At first it seemed a strange gamble for ambitious newcomers to acquire the mine, but, as their plans unfolded, his opinion changed. They pushed production immediately, bought nineteen more claims, lengthened the crosscuts, and used the Gem shaft to push fresh air into the mine. They jumped to the forefront of Butte Hill, pulling pure copper glance twenty-five feet thick from the Edith May and

19

Jessie veins. He helped them add ventilation fans, a new electrical system, and better drills. Before his eyes, the original dank workings changed to good moving air. The crosscuts now reached nine major veins and almost a thousand new men were added to the payroll. The shifting heavy ground and shut downs were replaced by a smooth running mine.

He took particular pride in the new Granite Mountain shaft and its quick sinking to more than 3700 feet through solid rock. They were among the first to move from steam power to electricity, and then they installed the most powerful electric hoist in the world.

Here in 1917, the promise seemed endless, and as foreman, he knew he was part of the best mine on the hill.

CHAPTER TWO

BRALY, SULLAU, AND THE SHIFT BOSSES

It was a busy Friday for Sullau. He got off work at two in the morning, spent nearly an hour putting together his notes for production, then slept through the shift whistle at eight and got up at ten. The last few hours were spent preparing for a discussion with manager Norman Braly, and Lester Frink the Superintendent, going over last month's progress and company planning for the rest of June. After that, he had a meeting with his night shift bosses before going to work at six. Another man might have enjoyed some quiet, but Sullau liked the work.

The main office at the Old Speculator yard was between the framing and carpenter's shop, the oil house, and the steel frame building where the service hoist engine was. Service work for the mine still went through the Old Spec shaft, but all direct hoisting of the miners and ore had been moved down the hill to the new Granite Mountain shaft.

Sullau's boots knocked heavy on the floor boards as he entered the room, the afternoon sun came through the dusty, small paned windows. A cold pot-bellied stove stood in the corner, with a desk, maps, and ledger drawers next to it. Braly and Frink were already at the small table. The day foreman Fritzberg was seated beside Braly.

"Have a seat Ernest," said Braly, gesturing to the unoccupied chair, "Let's get this finished."

Braly spoke with precision and listened closely, which Sullau appreciated. He had been a hands-on manager for the last several years, replacing CP Pope, a man the meticulous Sullau had worked hard under but never really liked. Pope had steered the new company since just after its start, an optimistic and energetic man, acquiring new claims with savvy dealing, wanting the best, pushing production. The company had quickly become very profitable, but over time he got distracted. Men change, particularly successful men in a gambling, brothel-filled, wide-open city.

Sullau was not surprised when Pope was let go for reasons he did not want to imagine. Whether the Board tired of rumors about a Butte mistress, extravagant use of company cars, or questioned expenses for cronies and parties, Sullau never knew. He was merely relieved that when the company went to hire a new manager, they chose a miner who understood what men needed to do their work right.

The manager's position took a man with years underground, who knew how to drill and shoot a round, who had an eye toward new equipment, yet could sharpen these things into budgets and present them to the bankers and Board members of the company. Sullau knew mining, but he did not know how to handle New York men, staring at you with new shirts and clean hands, and convince them of the needs of 1100 miners.

Given that the Speculator workings were infamous for hot bad air, it was a happy occurrence that Braly also was an expert in the new field of mine ventilation, and had taken it upon himself to fix that problem in the short time he had been there.

"President Cole says the Board of Directors is pissing about any turndown in production," said Braly. "Everybody thinks the war will push copper prices higher, so they want to take advantage. We did well the last two quarters. We're up twenty-five percent since last year."

They started through the list, Braly reading quickly and listening to brief replies. There was discussion of the different levels and sections of the mine, the output, how much timber they needed, how many feet of 18 gauge track, and the likely grade of ore from vein to vein. They had burned up the new 4000 horsepower electric hoist last year trying to lift thirty ton loads at forty miles an hour, which required a new design for the motor. That hurdle passed, and it was on to the next.

Braly read off the figures and they considered which drifts to drive further, what raises to push. The Speculator drifts on the 600 and 700 levels were advancing between ten and fifteen feet per week, sixty-four feet for the month. "All the ore is assaying close to five percent copper and good silver." Likewise the Adirondack and Jessie veins were producing well.

"On the 2200, we're drifting along the hanging wall of the Edith May. The ore is consistently six feet thick at the face, with excellent production. The new crosscuts over to the Adirondack, those went fast."

Braly stopped when it came to the ventilation. "I'm glad you proposed the pair of fans for the 2200 Edith May, Ernest. I was doubting at first, you know, the cost," he shrugged, "and running that cable out there. But they've done well. Who pushed for that?"

"Moore," said Sullau.

"Yeah, JD. Pass thanks to him. God knows it's a hot bastard down there."

The news was good out to the east as well. On the Snowball vein the geologists and engineers had traced a nice shoot of ore from the 1600 down through the 2000 level, averaging five feet wide, good grade copper and rich in silver. "Last assays showed up to twelve ounces a ton silver," Braly said, approvingly, "and seven percent copper."

They discussed sinking both shafts further, the Granite Mountain was already down to 3700 feet, the Speculator to nearly 3000.

"I told New York we should wait, finish the stations, 30, 32, 34, 36 first. Do the crosscutting. In six months, we can have stations down to the 3600. That'll open up six hundred vertical feet of those veins for stoping. We'll have good ore for the next two years."

"Got a good man on that crosscutting," said Sullau.

"Who?"

"John Collins, hired him four months ago."

"You know who to hire," Braly laughed. "That's why we're deeper than anybody."

Sullau broached a difficult topic. "Mr. Braly, keep in mind, rock temperature is over a hundred degrees down there, we'll need more fans."

Braly cocked his eyebrows, Sullau met the gaze evenly. He had learned Braly was open to ideas, but to push carefully. You had to stick a small piece of coal in the stove and wait for it to burn.

"I know," Braly finally said. "We have the new reverse fan on top here. I'll look at budgeting for smaller fans. That reminds me, compressor engineer says we're bleeding too much air from the drill system, men are leaving the air headers and hoses on when they aren't being used."

Sullau persisted, "That's because of the bad air, especially in the Edith May. Spec is a weak upcast that deep, and stoping is so tight they're not getting air." He looked Braly in the eye, "Is there any chance we can add a compressor?"

Braly thought about it, "Expensive. Have to clear it with New York."

"It would help the men."

"Let me push it. Takes time."

"If the veins split more, the drifting and stoping will get worse."

Braly nodded, "Agreed. But I have to convince the Board."

He turned back a page in the sheaf of notes and read it silently. "Okay, last update on the crosscuts. Crews did one hundred forty feet in the last week. It's coming fast."

He set down the papers and opened up a notebook on the table, filled with penciled tables identifying the tunnel and position of ore samples taken in the last two weeks, and their assayed amounts of metals. "Ernest, I'd like you to explain something to me. All of the samples below 2800 show one to three percent copper, even in the crosscut waste. That's almost production, and we're not in a vein," he said, his voice a mixture of surprise and skepticism. "What's going on?"

"I was down with Fiscus," said Sullau, "The rock is banded with ore stringers and horsetails. We're in some copper almost all the time, even between veins."

"Huh," said Braly, and nodded with approval, "That's good."

Sullau added, "Did you see the numbers when they hit the Hughes?"

24

Braly's face opened in a smile, "As a matter of fact I did." He flipped to a dog-eared page and looked around the table at the others. "Assays were six percent copper and fourteen percent zinc." He clapped the assay book closed and put it down. "We'll do damn well when we get this development work finished."

He picked up the notes again. "Final items," Braly said, "We still got repairs in the Speculator shaft. The men need to pull the safety bulkhead out at the 2000. Our electricians and ropemen will get the signal bells below 2200, put in signal pull bottles on the 22, and string the cords down to the 24. Maybe two days, then we'll have it open all the way down."

"Last thing. As you know, the Modoc fire set us back four weeks. The lesson is, a problem for one of us can spread to the rest. We're lowering the main electric cable in the Granite Mountain shaft today, down to the 2600. Your men can't use the chippy hoist, but when the cable's down, the electricians will connect the transformer and we'll have lights, the water pumps ready, and our sprinkler system. By tomorrow night, the fire prevention system should be finished. What happened in the Modoc won't happen to us."

"Damn fire is still smoldering," said Frink, shaking his head.

Sullau thought back. There were two fires in a row, a month apart in the Modoc. It was the Butte-Balaklava Company's mine, one claim over to the south. The first fire was an overheated electrical transformer at a lower station. The flames lit the wall timbers, spread into the shaft and burned it from top to bottom. The second, a trolley box on the 2200 carried the fire north into the Tuolumne. Both times, smoke pushed into the Spec through the crosscuts from the High Ore, and some into the stopes on the Jessie.

He remembered the rush to get his men out, running through the stopes, the frightened faces looking at him for direction. The gas from the burning timbers came into the south end of the Spec and quickly drove the miners back to the Granite Mountain shaft. There was a frantic scramble, six or eight were knocked out, but everybody got out alive. The mine was down for ten days. Then two weeks ago, it happened again, and everyone was on edge at the smell of smoke.

25

"The new High Ore manager called me, Chope's his name. A couple days ago they sealed off their drifts coming to us," said Frink. "Put in concrete doors in addition to our iron doors. Gas got through everything but the concrete. It's on 22, 24, and 28, for our men's safety. Said they'd take them down when the fire's out. But that's not going to be any time soon."

Frink looked closely at his notes and summarized the work on the manways, "Mine inspector's going to ding us couple places. I was through the 600 and 700 last week. Bad area. We've had to retimber a couple times. Got two problem manways, 651 and 652, but most of the rest have troubles too. There's still no station on the 600. Shift is hoisted to 700, and everybody climbs up and down those two manways to their stopes. Nearly sixty men. The rock's making water all through there. Geologists traced it, the groundwater sinks from the crest of the hill right into that damn level, always trouble with caving."

Sullau was blunt, he put his rock-roughed hands on the table, "The manways are there for the men. They must be solid."

"Get a timber crew on each one until they're good," said Braly, "Then keep them clear."

Braly ended the meeting. "Well, biggest thing, you know, boys are going to be drafted. Started yesterday. Thank God, we got through that without any fights Uptown. Nor a strike, but there sure could be. The war has people hot."

"Martial law and machine guns at the courthouse, that's probably why they thought better of it," offered Frink with a dry smile.

"Or maybe people kept their heads for once around here," said Braly. "But if miners are drafted, we'll have a manpower problem. Guess we'll deal with that if we have to."

He stood up and thanked them, "Have a good evening gentlemen. Tap 'er light."

Sullau left the meeting feeling satisfied. He walked through the hectic mineyard toward the Granite Mountain, three hundred yards north of the Speculator, through densely packed buildings, past the compressor and hoist houses, and around the slide where men struggled with giant loads of mine timbers dumped off the rail cars.

He mulled over the numbers they had talked about, the assays, total feet of crosscut, floors of raise in the stopes. Braly had good reason to be optimistic, and Sullau knew in his bones that as foreman he had to keep those numbers up.

But a thought lingered as he walked along the connecting road, trucks and wagons passing by. In hard rock, on the average it took an eight-hour shift of five good men drilling, blasting, mucking, and hauling, to get through a single foot of rock. With all those numbers, it was easy to lose sight of that simple fact. One shift, one foot.

He looked at the towering headframe in front of him, the locomotive chugging into place along the track, its huge cars below the chutes to the fifty-foot high ore bins. The Board members saw the tons of ore, the net costs and profit, dividends and the price of the stock. Braly saw the working mine, the veins and equipment, and how to get the ore into production.

And Sullau? Sullau saw the numbers, but he thought about the men.

***

When he came to the headframe, a group of electricians and ropemen were gathered around the shaft collar, ten hours after starting that morning and still lowering the electric cable. It was far underground, the near end was four hundred feet from the surface, the front end at the 1600 level. Sullau watched them for a few minutes without saying anything, and Hale, the head electrician came over.

"All smooth Sullau, done by eight, maybe nine."

"You'll pull it into the 26 crosscut? We need the chippy cage."

"Yep, it'll all be out of the way. Chippy will be back to you before half-shift tonight."

Sullau thanked Hale and prepared for his next meeting, waiting for his shift bosses. He sat in a small office in the building beside the headframe. Next door were the engineers and geologists, their cluttered desks lined one wall and shelves filled with notebooks and mining journals lined the other.

Taking up the east side of the building was a single large room with flat wooden shelves holding hundreds of mining maps, level after level, divided into checker-boarded sections according to vein, drift, and claim. In the middle, tables with high chairs and quivers of ink pens with a dozen different gauges. There, the draftsmen created their carefully inked drawings of the workings. Eight hours a day they took survey notes, geological sketches, measures of crosscutting and drifting, and translated them into meticulous maps showing more than fifty miles of tunnels, drifting ore veins and haulage ways. Colored pencils denoted different features, red meant ore, blue was for faults, orange for injection dikes. There were tiny script notes describing the mineralization and thickness of ore at precise points. It was like a gigantic set of treasure maps written in an arcane tongue, going down level by level more than three thousand vertical feet.

Sullau was pulled out of his reading by the timekeeper O'Keefe, who came in with a sheet of paper. "Mr. Sullau, here's the list of new men today, thirty-five of them."

Sullau nodded, "Thanks," and skimmed through the names. A few Irish, one Austrian or German, then a Finnish name. The rest were all eastern European. Serbs, Croatians, Greeks.

The usual these days, he thought with a sigh. It meant problems with language, difficulties telling them what to do, where to go. *Men with no mining experience*, he thought. That was the hardest. They were willing to work but damn, it was more important to keep them from getting hurt. When a man nodded but didn't comprehend, nobody around was safe, least of all him.

In his seventeen years in Butte, Sullau had seen men from forty countries. Most were fine, hard working, honest. They wanted a job. But he hated how ignorance in the mine could cost newcomers so dearly. Blisters and a sore back were one thing, broken bones and getting killed were another.

There were voices in the hallway, creaking wood floors and the clomp of footsteps as the day personnel began to leave. He set the paper down next to the other notes.

Outside, the early summer sun was up high in the west, and the June weather was cool but agreeable. Through the partly open window came the constant bang and racket of the busy yard, the smell of dust and oil, and the smoke from distant smelters down and around the hill to the south, the Parrot, Pittsmont, and Colorado. He could see the bottom half of the Granite Mountain headframe, hovering over him dark and imposing, the biggest one of all hundred mines on the hill.

The first shift boss came, Ben Tregonning, a clean-shaven Cornishman who had the crew deep at the 2800 level on the Edith May. He had been at the Tramway for years, possessed a quick mind and it was easy to see he could be a success at any job he worked. Sullau had been pleased when Tregonning accepted an offer of shift boss, although he had made it clear that at some point he intended to go back to his job as an insurance agent. Nobody expected him to be a shift boss forever.

Tregonning held out his hand, "Evening Foreman."

They shook hands. "Ben, good to see you."

Tregonning smiled, "Been meaning to talk, Sully," he said, using his nickname. Sullau's eyebrows raised slightly.

"Oh?"

"I've decided I'm going to go back to the insurance job. Appreciate working with you and the others, but it's time."

"When?"

"A couple of weeks or a month, so you need to find a replacement."

"Sorry you're leaving."

"Same, been a pleasure working for you."

"Hard to find men good enough to work deep," Sullau said. "I know that 2800's tough, with the heat and bad air."

Tregonning laughed, "Good ore though."

Sullau smiled slightly, "Yes, it is good ore." He looked at Tregonning again and thought, *A man's got to have mining in his blood to say that.*

The foursome from the west side appeared around the timber stacks alongside the idler towers, coming off the road from the Speculator, Bronson, Moore, Collins, and Weigenstein. Hard men in worn work clothes, lunch buckets and carbide lamps in hand, shift notebooks in their breast pockets.

They came into the office. Simple greetings around the group. "Boys," said Sullau, "How's she going?"

"Hey Boss."

"Mr. Sullau."

Goodell came down the trestle walkway over the rail line, followed by Hamill, McNichols, Fitzharris, and McFadden. Gorrie came along, talking with a group of his contract miners on the 2400.

Days pay miners had been trickling into the yard for an hour, napping or smoking alone on timber stacks to the side of the headframe, or chatting in small groups and shading their eyes from the slanting sun of the late afternoon. They paid scant attention to the bosses in the last of their free time before they went down. They would be on the job soon enough, somewhere in the vast sprawl of tunnels, earning the handsome sum of five dollars a day. For now, their time was their own.

At the top of the hour, the eleven shift bosses stood in the room together, serious faces and straight backs, notebooks in hand. They did not plan to stand there long, but take care of business and get on with the shift. It was a group that knew mining and were hired to tell men what must be done and expected their orders be followed.

The shift bosses directed nearly four hundred miners underground, from the Edith May and Adirondack veins on the west, to the Berlin vein more than a half mile to the east. From the 400 level down to the drilling teams crosscutting 3700 feet below surface, a well-organized army of men delved into the rock in search of ore.

Miners were like squads of soldiers and grenadiers, skirmishing along ore veins with their drills and dynamite, with ladders and tunnels connecting all their work to the shaft. They contended with the drilling, burrowing, blasting up and across the irregular sheets in the fractured granite of the hill, each group focused at a different level.

Weigenstein had fifty-seven men on the stopes between the 600 and 700 levels close to the Speculator shaft. Bronson's beat had forty-two in the Snowball vein far out in the north country, 24 to 2600 levels, toward the edge of the Badger. JD Moore's crews were between the 20 and 2200 of the north Edith May, as far west as you could be in the mine, a particularly difficult beat because the fractured rock funneled ground water into it, seeping through the fissures. It was the area that gave the Old Spec its reputation for bad air. The manager put his best men in places like that, or else he shut the stopes off. Here, with copper prices high and the new demand from the war, Braly was under orders to hit hard the places that produced.

Luther Goodell took the south half of the Edith May "ledge", where the vein split into several subparts, each of which they drifted along. Collins was the new hire, a terse and rough-edged man who oversaw the new crosscutting below 3000 feet where the mine would expand to the 32, 34, and below. His demeanor matched the work, a combination of slugging tunnels through solid rock and precisely linking them together. Like Collins, Ben Tregonning and his men worked farther down than any other miners on the hill, nearly 3000 feet. Tregonning's easy manner belied a sharp knowledge of his beat in the complex broken ore shoots of the Edith May and Hughes veins.

The shift bosses spoke in a pithy miner's slang. They were men of action, not of letters, their words like the chiseled edges of a steel drill bit. Their intelligence went to understanding the ways of the mine, the mineralization that made good ores, the placement and depth of drill holes and dynamite. Just as the precise minerals of the rock were formed from the pressure and temperature of the earth, their personalities were formed by hard-won experience of years in the mines. It was a pure meritocracy, no minced words and no bullshit. No one got to be a shift boss, much less a foreman like Sullau, without drive or without understanding how men made rock do what they needed. And in particular, what both men and rock did under pressure.

31

It was an education that had all the intricacy of any valedictorian's thesis, but written in action, sometimes in blood, chased by whiskey.

Sullau looked around at the men's strong faces and sharp eyes. *As good as any shift on the hill*, he thought with satisfaction, *Lucky to have them*. He cleared his throat and started.

He talked brusquely and to the point, his English tinted by the German his parents had always spoken at home.

He went through the production numbers Braly had outlined, the targets for tons of ore, how much had come out of each beat and vein. There were problems, and he pointed out which levels would need skip service.

"Fiscus and his crew will be assaying on the 22 and 24, Edith May. The ore is good, five percent and more, every stope is producing. Help him out as he comes through. Use it to teach your new men about the ore. Ignorant miners are poor miners," he said.

"Edith May and Snowball are the biggest producers right now." He looked at Moore and Goodell, to Gorrie and Tregonning whose beats were on the Edith May, then over to Bronson and Hamill, "We got high grade ore. Let's keep it up."

He drew his finger down the list of points. "Last week's report was good. For the month we're up twenty percent in tonnage, this week's looking about the same. Braly is happy. If you have any delays, problems, let me know."

He flipped through the next several pages, "Got ninety new ore cars. Blacksmith's shop is finishing them up, I checked and they have thirty ready to go. When you need them, tell Barnicoat to send them down to your level."

He turned to Weigenstein, "Braly ordered two timbering crews working on the 651 and 652 manways, so expect them there. Keep your men from running them over. We'll send the timber down the Spec shaft. Braly wants them worked on until they're finished and in good shape."

"Everybody..." he pressed the table with the palm his thick hand, "There's a cable going down the Granite Mountain pump compartment, so we don't got the chippy hoist for a bit. Electrician tells me they'll be done by mid-shift, then the chippy will be back to us."

He looked over at Bronson, "Jack, they're pulling in the cable on your 2600, to the north. Your motorman will have to help."

"I'll have him check in with them," said Bronson.

The only sheet of paper that remained was the list of new men. Sullau picked it up, "Timekeeper says we got thirty-five new men on this shift. They're on the 1800 and 2400. Put them with good partners, not mucking ten floors up in a sun room. Start them in a place they can get the hang of things. They all say they're miners, but…, you know the story. They don't know anything."

"Moore, that area heading out to the northwest, the big crosscut…?"

Moore looked up, "Yeah, the 2254."

"Braly's happy about that fan. Crews there are cutting fast, and already in Adirondack ore. He says to pass on a thanks." It was hard to tell how men took compliments, they were so few and far between, but Moore felt good about being singled out. He had gone out on a limb demanding the extra expense for his boys, and he was pleased it had worked out.

"Collins, we've got extra drill steel for that harder section you were in last three days, so tell your nipper to take it down. I've already talked with the blacksmith shop. They know."

"And the rest of you, watch the men leaving the hoses and headers open. We got complaints from the compressor plant. Five, six times the last couple of days we were down to half the pressure we should be, fifty pounds per square inch last few shifts. That's not much faster than hand drilling. Talk with your drill crews, close the valves on the hoses not drilling. If we bring the pressure back up, we can make even better progress."

Tregonning spoke up, "Boss, the 2800 is over a hundred degrees. The stopes off the Spec shaft are tight. Guys leave them hoses on because it's bad, even on the first couple of floors."

"I talked to Braly about that," said Sullau. "We'll look into fans. But it'll have to wait until after the new cable is in. Braly got the heavier cable, upped the voltage so it can run the extra load. And I asked him about a new compressor."

Around the table, Sullau could feel the men's interest and smiled wryly at them, "Yeah, I did, and he was okay with pushing the budget for it. Don't want you and your men working in a hell hole."

A few more minutes and they were through. Sullau went down the hall to his small office, while several of the shift bosses jotted down short lists in their notebooks. The group from the west side, Moore, Bronson, Weigenstein and Collins, walked over together to their counters near the shaft, checking the no-shows, giving assignments for the contract miners and days pay men, laying out plans for their shift.

The day shift miners had left and most of the four hundred men of the night shift had already been lowered. Barnicoat stood by the shaft collar, joking with the last groups of men. Tregonning talked animatedly with one of his lead miners on the 2800, George Felutovich, as they waited below the headframe.

Another set of big cages came up and Barnicoat said, "Okay, first eight here, quick like." Men squeezed in and he closed the doors and rang to lower to the next cage. "Next group now." He worked the bells smoothly and for the last cage, he motioned Tregonning in with one of his stoping crews, headed to the lower Edith May. Tregonning and Felutovich got on together, still bantering, the first in a Cornish-tinged voice and the second in a thick Serbian accent with broken grammar. Moore stood behind for the next set of cages, like waiting for the trolley to take them to work.

Barnicoat greeted Moore and rang the bells for the other set of cages on the counterbalanced shaft. "Hey Jimmy, you and the bosses will go down with the rest of Tregonning's crew." He nodded to the shift bosses as they waited, "Albert, Jack,…"

Shortly, they got on with the last of the men. The cages dropped down the shaft, jostling back and forth from the slight bends in the teak wood guides, and the familiar thin burning smell filled their noses as the steel slid over the teak at eight hundred feet per minute.

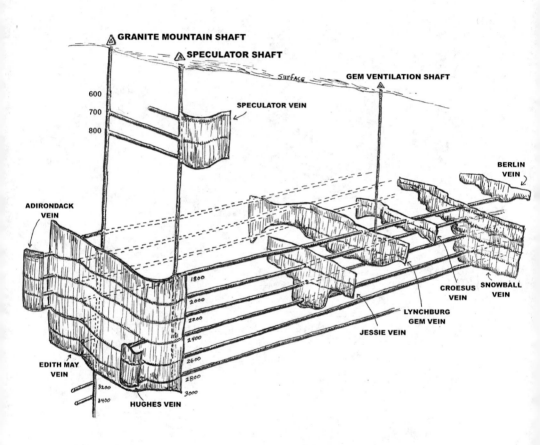

Major ore veins of the Speculator Mine, June 1917

CHAPTER THREE

MOORE'S BEAT

At the 2200, station tender Pete Sheridan racked the cage doors open and Moore stepped out. He turned and gave a wave to Bronson, Collins, and McFadden, as the door closed and they continued to the lower levels.

The station was a high chamber blasted out of the granite, wider than the four compartments of the shaft, with thick square-cut timbers tight against the roof. The floor extended away from the shaft, connecting to the crosscuts and rail tracks. A half-dozen bare bulbs hung across the top, spreading light on the dusty rock room. Below Moore's feet, metal turnsheets covered the ground so the tenders could push and spin loaded tram cars on and off the cages.

Fifteen feet from the station on the edge of the turnsheets were the ore pockets, holes covered by the metal grills of the grizzlies, where the trains of loaded cars dumped ore directly from the tracks. At the far edge of the sheets, rails started and continued out to the main crosscut tunnel of the mine.

Moore stood beside Sheridan, peering down into the ore pocket. From the loading deck below the station, echoing up through the shaft, came the sounds of harsh muttering.

"Gate's stuck. Conroy's clearing it," said Sheridan. "Had some trouble with the last skip. Could only load it halfway."

There was loud clanging of metal on metal followed by cursing. Sheridan gave a little snort, "Yeah, he's fixing it alright."

Conroy poked his head up and tossed a pry bar out, bouncing across the turnsheets, and hauled himself out of the loading deck covered in dust.

"Eh Michael, how's she goin?" asked Moore.

Conroy spit, "She ain't. She's goddamned stuck. Piston rod's bent. Can't dump."

"But the other's good?" Moore pointed to the pocket on the left side.

"It's goddamn fine."

Fist-sized pieces of ore lay on the floor at their feet, spilled from the last dumping. Moore kicked one into the opening of the other ore pocket. It skipped over the raised edge and ricocheted down into the holding area thirty feet below. "Call Barnicoat and get a blacksmith down here."

"Yeah," Conroy shook his fist down at the broken gate.

"Motor's coming next hour. We got to have a place for that trip of ore," said Moore.

Conroy nodded and waved his hands, exasperated. "Already called up half hour ago, ain't come down yet."

"Well, call again, tell him I said the men are pulling rock out and we need both pockets."

"With pleasure, Boss," said Conroy.

Just beyond the station, the tracks split. One set of rails went into the north country of the mine, the Jessie, Lynchburg and Snowball veins. The other into the south country of the Edith May.

Moore's boots scraped over the ore grit and walked by a line of empty cars whose ore had just been dumped into the pockets. A dusty north country motorman lifted his hand in silent greeting to Moore, then bent down to hitch the cars onto his train, readying to pull them back to the Croesus drifts.

Glancing down the 2275 crosscut into the north country, Moore turned right, heading south to his beat in the Edith May. A drainage ditch seeped water next to the rock wall, and Moore watched his step along the worn path between the rails. Reaching the first switch, he turned left onto the 2202 drift that followed the Edith May vein south toward stope 18. It was halfway to the Speculator shaft, the start of his beat.

As he went, he had his notepad out and kept track of everything that needed attention. On the right side, there was rock broken off the ribs, blocking the drainage ditch. *Get the nipper to toss it into a waste stope.* The westside timber around the fortieth set was taking weight, bulging slightly. *Need to relieve pressure.* Right next to it was a fissure making water with fault gouge sloughing out of it. *Put lagging in to keep it off the tracks.*

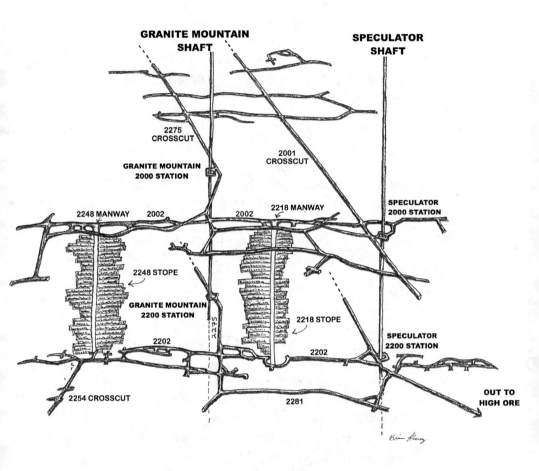

Moore's beat on the 2000 and 2200 levels of the Speculator Mine along the Edith May vein.

Reflexively he scanned the water pipes and compressed air lines, listening for leaks, watching for dripping.

All along the drift were signs of ore after the miners had hollowed out the vein, little stripes of peacock green a finger's width wide, with too much waste rock between them to mine. Some areas along the top of the tunnel were shored up with planks where they had stoped above, but much of the rock was left to keep the ground from settling. That was a bigger problem further south along the drift, especially near the Old Spec shaft where the ore vein actually crossed the shaft. The thought reminded Moore, *Didn't Sullau say the Spec retimbering was done and they're putting in signal bells? Better check that today.*

Beside him the rock walls glistened, streaked and discolored, where water seeped from cracks. In the raises above, it dripped down manways onto the ladders, crusting and sliming the rungs, freezing like cement and making chutes muckbound. It was a nasty area to work, hard to drill in the fractured rock and the wetness often delayed fuses. What he hated the most was a round that shot in the wrong order, or worse, not at all. Hangfires and missed holes could maim or kill men when the fuses crept, stopped, then suddenly flared and exploded the dynamite as men checked the face. Such was the deep Edith May vein.

Across the hill, and especially in the Speculator, it was well known among miners that JD Moore had the skill to deal with such problems, keep his men safe, and get rock in the box. He understood the problems of the Edith May from years in the silver mines of Nevada's infamous Comstock lode, where men could only work fifteen minutes out of each hour because of the sweltering heat, and were given fifty pounds of ice a day to cool themselves. He had come to Butte like all the men did, for a better job. His first mine, the Colorado, hired him as a shift boss, then the next year he moved to the Mountain Con. The Speculator staff enticed Moore away from that job when a position came open on their 2200, and he quickly learned its peculiarities.

In 1917, all miners and timbermen, muckers and samplers did their work in a few square feet of light amidst the darkness, lit only by candle or small carbide lamps. For decades, the surveyors whose job it was to lay out the tunnels within a fraction of an inch every hundred feet, worked with the illumination from the flickering wick and melting wax of a candle. They had only been replaced in 1916 by the steadier flame of the carbide lamps.

Moore bought a new carbide lamp that lasted several hours, but his underground habits stuck close. He always kept two candles in his pocket and a waterproof canister of matches, because if the lamp fell into the mud, he was stuck in the dark fumbling to clean the burner tip and dry the flint. A candle could be cut, wiped, and relit in twenty seconds.

He was partial to the candles for other reasons too. The flame's color and size said immediately how much oxygen was in the air, or whether there was gas, the invisible killer. And although he would not admit it to anybody, the little flame's living flutter calmed him in a way the thin whistle of the carbide did not.

He caught a glimpse of a carbide lamp one hundred feet ahead of him, moving with the shadows of walking men. Moore recognized the gaits. It was two of the contract miners coming on shift, Roberts and Wynder, headed toward the 2218 stope, where they directed a crew on the fourth floor.

Seeing a man's black outline once, he could recognize it as well as a face he had seen on the street at mid-day. That worked both ways, and the savvy among his men knew their shift boss at a glance when they saw his distinctive light. The bright, bluish tinge from the carbide and aggressive spring-like walk meant one person, "Tin Can" Jimmy Moore. A man who brooked no guff and would "can" a miner in a second if he screwed up, but hire him right back if the lesson was learned. The men respected him because no better miner lived than Jimmy, and they did not mind a boss who was temperamental, as long as he was fair.

A motor's low hum gradually filled the tunnel and a headlight appeared, jarred, and bounced in the air in front of him, growing brighter. He could hear the sound of full cars rumbling on the track, headed toward the station from the south of his beat. He stepped to the side and waited.

The motorman saw the bright lamp and rang his bell.

41

Moore signaled, shaking his head side to side and holding up his hand. The train stopped next to him.

"Hey Boss," said the motorman.

"You're on it early."

The motorman straightened his back and propped an elbow on the housing, a cigarette held between his fingers. He motioned behind him. "Yeah, Jackson from day shift. Told me up top he left the train by stope 18. Said they was slow loading. Thought I'd come down early, get the trip to the station."

"You get the 18 and 20 chutes?"

"Just pulled them."

Moore nodded approval and motioned back towards the station. "Right ore pocket's stuck, use the left."

"Yeah, Conroy was working on it when I was there." The motorman took a drag on his cigarette and blew a stream of smoke from pursed lips. "That is, if bitchin' is workin'." He smiled again and laughed, "Just joking, Conroy's a good man."

"You going to pull the chutes on the north side? We need to keep them moving."

"Next trip."

"If I don't see you out there, check the short runs at the far north end, they're drifting in good ore on both sides of the split vein. Pick up any loaded cars around there, and check the 54 crosscut, the one with the new fan. They've been in ore last couple days."

Moore was about to let him go, but remembered, "There's a section of track out on the 2202 northwest, spikes missing. Get it solid. Take the days pay miners from the short drift."

Moore stepped back, ready to get on with his beat.

"Will do." The motorman said and gave Moore a little salute. He swiveled the control lever forward and the low electric humming rose in pitch as the locomotive started moving, sparks snapping from the trolley rod above.

As the motor went by, the swamper sat silent and grinning on the back, and touched the brim of his grimy hat in a gesture of parting to the shift boss. The ore train headed away down the track toward the Granite Mountain station, loaded cars clattering behind.

The familiar activity of the mine filtered into Moore's ears, the beat and pulse of distant hammering, knocking of water pipes, and slight vibration of the rails through his boots. Walking another few hundred feet to stope 2218, he heard the heavy chuff of a big slugger drill just beyond in Goodell's beat, advancing a drift to the west. Stopping at the 2218 manway, from many floors up came the higher pitched buzz of stoper drills, lighter machines the men could manhandle around in the narrow spaces. Closer by, the smack of sharp hammer strokes and the murmur of men's voices sifted down the manway.

In the stope above him, men worked upwards and sideways following the narrow sheet of the vein, hollowing out the ore like the inside of a wafer, floor by seven-foot floor. When they were done burrowing upwards to the 2000 level, perhaps in several months, the stope would have twenty-eight floors timbered, spreading out sideways to strip the rich vein from between the granite walls.

At the opening of the manway the rock rumbled down the chute to his side. Larger pieces thumped against the thick planks protecting his ladderway, then clashed against the metal gate that the motorman had just closed. The contract miners above, Wynder and Roberts on the fourth floor, were going at it hard with their muckers shoveling the ore down the chute.

He rapped on the compressed air pipes to tell the men above he was coming up, then blew out his lamp and hung it on the top button of his coat. Grabbing the wooden ladder rungs of the manway, he started climbing into stope 18.

The Edith May vein was a giant sheet of copper ore sloping vertically into the earth, ranging from a few inches to twenty-five feet thick. It formed an inclined plane half a mile long, parallel to the Great Divide, starting near the surface and extending down thousands of feet. North to south, it stretched from the Badger claim, through the Speculator, then into the High Ore claim.

There were many other such veins across ten square miles on the Butte hill, spreading out from deep inside the granite batholith. Each vein was wrinkled with hidden pockets and horse-tail tendrils of copper ore, mixed in different places with silver, lead, zinc, and bits of gold. Big veins split, forming an irregular checkerboard, in some places pinching out to nothing. For thousands of feet below the surface, as far as they had mined and more, the hill was a complex pattern of faults and veins. But for all the meticulous mapping that was done, the truth was always in the drill and blast.

No matter how long men had been underground, the eagerness was the same after a round was shot, the dust settled, and the smoke drawn away. They all felt the desire to find out *What's there?* A blast might show a blank wall of granite. Or the round might reveal an entire face of solid copper glance, metallic sulfide rock called peacock copper, so brilliantly colored that even in the candlelight men looked in amazement and felt as if they had unlocked a secret vault.

Moore climbed up the manway by feel, until he reached the landing thirty feet up on the fourth floor of the stope where the first contract crew was working. Their candles shown dimly in the raise as he stepped onto the floor and relit his lamp.

The air was filled with fine rock dust from the drilling, floating like a haze. He walked along the narrow passageway heading toward the sound of a drill, noting with approval that the extra air hose was wound carefully and hung on the timber to the side, the tools were in order, hammers, three shovels, two scaling bars, and the drill steel sorted by length. The square set timbering above him was solid, every wedge carefully placed tight along the caps.

Off the end of the timbers, Wynder was at the face drilling a set of holes, his stoper drill clattering. Roberts was right behind him looping the compressed air hose to keep it out of their way. Their mucker Voko threw the last shovelfuls of ore into a large wheelbarrow to dump into the chute.

Moore stood and watched from behind. Percussive vibration filled the narrow tunnel. He heard it with his teeth as much as his ears. He could tell by the higher pitch of the stoper they were in good ore. The mineralized rock was harder than the granite around it, flaking, and the drill had a metallic bark from the sharp recoil. All around them was the pungent smell of the sulfide ore.

In the dim light, he could make out that the holes were more narrowly placed than usual, Moore furrowed his brow, but knew Wynder had a steady hand on the drill and was a good judge of placement. The point was to maximize the ore shot from a round.

Roberts slapped Wynder on the shoulder and motioned back toward Moore. Wynder glanced around, his moustache was covered in light dust like a frost and smears of mud ran across his forehead and chin. He turned the drill off and clapped the grit from his hands.

Moore nodded to Wynder, "How's she going?"

"Nice rock in here," said Wynder, hesitating, deciding what to say. "Roberts and I was thinking, if you're good with it, we can maybe even do a round at lunch, then another at end shift. Get two rounds in. Twice the ore."

Moore mulled it over, "Think so?"

"Want to push it where we can."

Moore was noncommittal, "Them are pretty narrow holes."

"Last couple of rounds I've been going in six feet, and we don't need more powder to blast it out. Can save two, three holes a round."

"Got no complaint about that," Moore said. He pointed at the line of side holes, "You're narrow here, you going to put two holes farther out?"

"No. This rock's breaking easy, and I don't want the blast to shoot into the timber. If I need to, I'll go wider next set. Rather do that than take a timber out and us have to reset the wood."

Moore smiled to himself and nodded.

Wynder said, "Fiscus was in here this morning, taking samples. Said ore's maybe eight percent."

Moore's eyebrows went up, the old one-armed sampler was a favorite of his, "Good money. Where's he now?"

"Went down to the 2400, through Goodell's 17 stope next door."

"You're looking good here," said Moore. "Let me see how the other floors are doing. I'll be back through in three hours. We can figure whether to shoot a lunch round. I'll make sure the motorman gets the powder and primers."

Moore went back to the ladder, coughing from the dust in his throat. It was a frequent argument they had about wetting down the muck, and Wynder would never relent. Wynder was using a dry stoper and preferred dry-drilling. Moore hated the dust. It got into everything, he ate it in his lunch, and he felt it in his chest when he left the mine. Old miners called the dry stoper drill a "widow-maker" and they coughed and wheezed after spending years in dusty stopes. Wynder had flatly told Moore he would rather have the dust than the goddamned mud. It was a constant battle, but Wynder had a sense for ore, so Moore relented.

On the tenth floor, he knew he would have to take extra time and his responsibility wore heavily. It was a group of new men, days pay miners he had paired with an old timer so they wouldn't make bad mistakes, and set them to mucking and timbering a newly blasted face.

He noticed something was wrong when he came off the ladder. Rock and tools were scattered on the floor. A group of three men stood at the far end, a hanging roof of rock over their heads. The old timer was not to be seen.

"Where's Olaf?" demanded Moore.

46

"Sick, I guess," said one. "Ain't here."

Moore took his lamp and looked quickly around, feeling alarmed. *This green crew shouldn't be working without oversight.* He scowled at the cluttered floor and noticed the floor planks were loose, with wide spaces between. *A man could break his leg falling through...* He peered down at the last timber set where the group of men were gathered and squinted at the rock over their heads. The last blast had left the back and ribs loose, and they had not barred down the broken rock above them.

That was too much. "For Christ's sake, get the hell out of there!" he ordered the men and stepped past, scanning the ribs and back. Cracks caught his attention, running up the face and over him.

His eyes sharpened, anger welling up. "Give me that," he pointed at a six foot scaling bar. A man passed it to him and reached up with the end, tapping the roof. It drummed with a hollow sound.

Moore exploded. "What the hell are you doing working here with that hanging over you?" he asked. "You hear that? That's the sound of a dead man!"

Stepping up into the closest man's face, Moore growled, "Didn't Olaf show you what to do?"

The men awkwardly glanced at each other.

"What're we going say to your wife when your bones are broken like you been through a stamp mill? Not on my beat."

He looked across the group, "From now on, if Olaf ain't here, then send somebody to find me, and don't do anything unless I tell you to."

"You two!" he yelled at the closest men. "Pop them slabs down with the bar before they kill somebody. And stay under the damn wood while you're doing it!" He grabbed another's shoulder, motioning above the first timber set. "See that? Put a stull right there. Cut it to fit and wedge it tight, so that rock don't come down and brain you." He tossed the bar and it landed in a clang and a puff of dust on the boards. "And damn it, clean the rock off the floor and nail down the lagging."

Moore went on directing every man, knowing the entire

47

time that if they did not already have the fear of God in them, he better put it there. He watched them scurry, barking an order when anyone slowed down, then finally stopped everything, saying, "Okay, take five."

He motioned them over, "None of you has been here long enough to work alone. I'm going to send another miner up here to help Olaf and you boys. Do everything he says."

Then he looked from one man's face to the next, speaking in a low sober voice, "Never go under loose rock, or let your partner. Watch each other's back. He's going save your life. You'll save his. That's the way it is down here."

***

Moore was behind schedule when he reached the 2000 sill, two hundred feet directly above the drift he had come in on, at the southern end of his beat. He glanced at his watch and started back toward the northwest.

There were several small stopes along the way, and he ducked in, inspecting progress of the single crews, and hurried past the 2075 crosscut back to the Granite Mountain shaft, which split his beat into north and south halves. It took him twenty minutes to reach the northern half of the Edith May, preparing to climb through the 48 stope, where there were fourteen men working at different levels. Turning into the narrow manway, he started down the two hundred feet of ladder in the dark.

Floor by floor, Moore checked in with his men. The big Swede, Ole Erickson, was drilling his fifth hole. Nipper Mulderig had been by to get them new steel to replace the dulled bits. He talked briefly with the drilling team on the fifth floor, Truax and Sullivan, who had been on his beat for the last four months. He waved at two of his older and long-time men, Lisa and his partner Laszkeics, a quiet man who had been in the Edith May south country for the last two years and could out-shovel anybody.

Marthey and Garrity, the youngsters, were muckers. Marthey had more experience, Garrity just a couple months.

48

Garrity was on the first floor, breaking up the bottom muckbound part of the chute. A pile of rock chunks had wedged and the finer wet ore cemented in around. Heavy stabs with the steel bar cracked a chunk in half, then he worked the muck, prying into it against the thick planks of the chute until it fell out in wet hunks.

"That's good, keep it moving," Moore said to them approvingly.

Garrity looked up and gave a quick grin in the candlelight, then went back to it. Moore nodded with satisfaction, lit his lamp, and stepped onto the 22 sill.

***

At the 2200 station, two days pay miners stood listening to the tender Conroy. Beside them, Conroy had just loaded a flat rail truck with lagging boards stacked high, canvas bags of nails, wooden wedges, and hammers on top.

"You been to the Edith May ledge, ain't cha?" asked Conroy.

The days pay men, Otto and Marcus, glanced sidelong at each other and Marcus nodded hesitantly.

"Okay," Conroy pointed down the crosscut and their eyes dumbly followed. "Take this straightaway, then turn right at the first switch. Stay on the main drift, make a left at the third switch. Look to your right. Find the fan at the 2254." Conroy looked at his watch. "Moore's probably out there and he'll be picky about where you unload. Stack it near the fan and out of the way."

Conroy looked at them, "You hear what I'm saying?"

"Uh, yeah," Otto said, and pulled Marcus along, "We know."

They left the 2200 station pushing the rail truck and rolled to the first switch, turned right and went all the way out on the main drift. They dutifully counted the switches but the tunnels split when the vein did, and they had the choice of two different drifts in two directions.

"Which is the main drift?" asked Marcus.

"Don't know," said Otto. "It all looks the same."

They shrugged their shoulders and took the tunnel going to the right, not realizing there were small crosscuts one after another, leading back to the left tunnel. They turned at the next switch and in a few minutes they had done a complete circle.

"Where's these tunnels going?"

"We got's to stay on the main drift, Marcus."

"Say what?

"Conroy said, third switch up on the 2202. One to the left."

"But ain't this the fourth?"

"What?

"I say, the fourth?"

"No, it's the third, after the main switch."

"Huh," Marcus said, pushing back his cap, "third, fourth. I never been out here."

"Well, I neither, but it's this one," Otto said, pointing to the fan.

"Oh yeah, he said the fan."

"All this pushing makes a man tired," grinned Otto, "Gonna take me a break." He lit a cigarette.

They were aimlessly chatting, leaning on the loaded rail truck when Moore's light appeared out of the 48 manway, not fifty feet from them. The flash caught their attention and they watched it closely as Moore's quick footsteps crunched on the sill.

"Blue light coming,'" Otto said and snuffed his cigarette. "Moore don't like me," he whispered. "If he asks, tell him I'm at the honey car," and slipped into the crosscut next to the fan. He crept back into the dark and wedged himself out of sight behind an upright timber.

Moore walked up and stopped. He had seen the glow of two cigarettes. "Hey boys," he said loudly.

"Mr. Moore," said Marcus nervously.

"Where'd your buddy go?"

"He went, uh, to the honey car..."

Moore called into the dark crosscut through the cigarette smoke, "Hide faster next time." Otto cringed behind his cramped timber.

Turning to Marcus he added, loud enough that Otto could hear, "Both of you, finish your work."

"Stack those boards on the other side of the fan, right there against the rib," he showed them with his light, pointing at the wall. "Nails on top, saw, hammers too. We're putting trolley boxes and rails into the back of this 2254 crosscut. Make it neat."

He turned and walked down the drift thinking, *Jesus, these guys*....

When his footsteps had faded, Otto skulked out from his hiding place, tightened the cord around his waist to keep his pants up and muttered, "Yeah, yeah. You stop to catch a breath and there's Tin Can Jimmy, kicking you back in."

"Normal-wise, he'd just fire you," said Marcus.

Otto mumbled a curse and finished stacking the boards and tools. "Let's get out of here," and they wheeled the empty flat truck back toward the station.

Moore hurried along, checking in with the small crews farther out. On his way back it took him ten minutes to walk to the end of the 2254 crosscut, where he spoke briefly with the team there. They were in good ore and ready to tram a loaded car out to the end for the motorman. He left thinking, *Things are ship-shape*.

By eleven he had completed the first round through his beat, made his notes, and headed across the main 2202 back to the south end at stope 18.

CHAPTER FOUR

LOWERING THE CABLE

The North Butte company had been moving from steam and compressed air to electricity in every way they could. They were on the verge of being the first fully electrified mine. The latest addition was to construct a line of water sprinklers down the entire shaft. Each level would have its own electric water pump and tank and the system would put out any fire. With the new cable in place, they could finish it.

The Modoc fire goaded them to action. Just down the hill from the Speculator, the smoke had driven men out of five mines, including the Spec. A short circuit in a high voltage transformer lit the dry timbers in the shaft, burned more than two thousand feet of it. In a few short days the fire ruined years of work and nearly cost dozens of miners their lives.

"I'll be damned if we're going to make the same mistake," Braly said, vowing to solve the problem. They blasted out a room two hundred feet down the crosscut from the 2600 station, and set the new transformer there, away from the dry timbers of the shaft. The last step would be to connect the system together with the new electric cable.

Before daylight on Friday, a group of men worked on the surface by the Granite Mountain shaft, preparing to lower the high voltage cable. The cable was coiled on a huge reel, all twelve hundred feet of it, weighing three tons. Below the men, the shaft dropped 3700 feet to the sump.

The shaft was divided into four compartments. The two for the ore skips were each five by five feet, side by side, and each typically had one ore skip, or at shift change, sets of four big cages for hoisting the men. They were run by counterbalancing, one side going up as the other side went down. The third compartment was for hoisting men, called the chippy, and alongside it was three feet of extra space, a small area called the pump compartment, where the compressed air line, the water pipes, signal bells and electrical cables all ran vertically down into the mine.

The men took the steel hoist cable off the chippy cage and fed it down the pump compartment, ready to attach the electric cable to it. The engineer rigged an auxiliary hoist and they looped its cable over the sheave wheel on the headframe, down to the chippy compartment.

The armored high voltage cable defined the state of the industry. It was two inches thick and carried the electricity for all the lights, ventilation fans, pumps, and the fire prevention system. The best insulator men could find for the new cables and their large gauge copper wires was a thick layer of oily fabric, tarred cambric, hemp, and jute. This inner core of fabric was protected by a smooth, armored lead sheath.

Just before nine in the morning, they began lowering. Two men controlled the brakes for the giant reel of electric cable and two more electricians were in the chippy cage, chief electrician Hale, and his deputy, Bolitho. A sheave wheel was placed so the electrical cable came off in the center of the pump compartment, next to the vertical chippy hoist cable.

Hale rang the signal bells to lower the cage. The men on the brakes began releasing the electric cable. He rang to stop it every thirty feet, to allow three ropemen at the shaft to tie the two cables together. They stood with lengths of hemp ready, on small landings down in the shaft, each man ten feet lower than the one above.

The men controlling the giant spool of electric cable rode the brakes on the reel, so it matched the descending chippy cage.

"She's heavy. Keep her slow," ordered the boss ropeman, Ivar Rhude. He stood broad-shouldered at the shaft, overseeing the ropemen. A skip tender asked, "Hey Rhude, how you's doing that?"

Rhude smiled, picked up a four-foot length of hemp and brandished the end in the tender's face. "We takes this yarn," he said, and gripped the hoist cable and the electric cable, just below where it came off the sheave wheel.

"We takes the yarn and comes right over and around them both cables, like this. Seven, eight times. See?" He quickly twisted the rope tightly around both cables. "And we takes each end between the two cables, and we ties them back together." He secured the ends together to finish a tautly wrapped noose of hemp rope that bound the cables together. Nodding with satisfaction, he pointed a rough-knuckled finger at the knot, "And she holds."

He motioned to the men controlling the reel of electric cable. They released the brakes, the reel slowly fed out another thirty foot section. When it stopped, he picked up the next length of hemp and started another knot. "Now, three yarns more." He pushed heavily on the tender's shoulder so the man had to lean down, his face a foot from the cable. "You looks close. See her? And them two men below, they tie yarns too." His hands flashed effortlessly, and he snugged up the finished knot in front of the tender's nose and clapped him hard on the back. "Yeah, she no slip now."

The station tender went back to his post, understanding the knots better than he wanted, and the cable slowly spooled another thirty feet down into the compartment.

Below in the chippy shaft, the electricians worked from the cage, reaching through the timbers that divided the pump and chippy shafts, guiding the lead end of the three ton cable through the compartment, alongside water and compressed air pipes, five other cables, the sprinkler heads and brackets. As they went farther down the shaft, the free-hanging cable was so heavy it swung achingly slow.

It was a twelve-hundred foot, three-ton weighted pendulum strung precisely down a three-by-five foot shaft. They signaled the hoist engineer for every move, bells ringing to lower the cage a few feet at a time, sometimes only six inches, then stop. Raise a bit to pry the cable's end off a bracket, then ring again for down, making sure the cable dropped cleanly every foot along the way, hour after hour.

It was nearly nine in the evening, twilight had come and the bright lights were on. The men had been working for seventeen hours and the end of the electric cable was down to the 2600 level. All they had to do was loosen the end from the hoist cable, pull it into the 2600 station, and back to the new transformer. Then they could connect the pumps and fire sprinklers, the ventilation fans and lights, into the new system.

"You boys take a rest," said Hale to his men with a tired smile. "I'm going to see how she looks."

Hale got in the chippy cage and rang the bells, the hoist engineer raised him as he checked the cable. He saw something he didn't like. For the last two hundred feet, the cables were wound around each other. *Must have spun as it went down. Need to get the end loose*, he thought.

He lowered back down to the 2600, and told Bolitho, the assistant electrician, "I'm going to take out some of the stoppers to take the twist out, and then we'll loop the cable into the station." He got back in the cage and rang to be raised, five feet at a time, reaching into the pump compartment to untie the hemp lengths.

He could hear full loads of ore whizz by in the other compartments, slightly shaking the shaft even though separated by heavy liner boards. *Those miner boys are busy down between the 2600 and 2800*, he thought. He worked his way up, untying the knots. Fifty feet, then one-hundred feet.

"We'll have the twists out shortly!" Hale called down to Bolitho.

Bolitho waited below, standing at the opening to the shaft on the 26 station. "Gives me the willies," he said to the station tender. "How far down is the bottom?"

"Thousand feet," said the man, and gave a menacing smile. Bolitho reflexively backed away from the opening.

Movement in the pump compartment caught Bolitho's eye, and he peered closely at the cable, "Did you see that?" he asked the station tender.

"What?"

"Cable's slipping."

"I don't see nothing," said the other man.

Bolitho stuck his head into the compartment to look closely, the cable hanging just a few feet away. It crept downward. "She's moving. I swear it."

He yelled up the shaft, "Mr. Hale! Something's wrong."

"What is it?" came Hale's voice.

"Cable's coming down!"

Hale heard the cry with his hands undoing a hemp knot. He felt the heavy cable yank and slip several inches through the knot, the smooth lead surface slowly moving right before his eyes.

"Well, goddamn..."

Bolitho yelled, "Get out of the shaft!"

Hale yanked on the bells, ringing furiously to lower. The chippy cage went down, and his eyes were riveted on the thick cable only three feet from his head, dropping right with him. It sped up, faster and faster, began looping around the timbers separating the compartments, catching on the brackets. He reached the station and dove out of the cage, ran with Bolitho away from the shaft, the station tender right behind them. Then the cable cut loose.

The three men stood cringing at the back of the station as the heavy loops thrashed by, a crescendo of slapping and whipping against the timbers and turnsheets where they had been standing. All twelve-hundred feet of it came down in a coiling avalanche of metallic squeals and sharp snaps, stripping water pipes free and shattering them, rupturing its lead outer sheath and strewing the fabric insulation everywhere.

It took several minutes before debris stopped falling from above. For a while, a stream of water splashed until somebody turned off the valve farther up the shaft. The dripping slowed, then stopped. None of the men dared to stick his head into the shaft to look.

"Damn," said Hale. "What the hell happened?"

When the noises had finally settled, he got on the chippy cage with Bolitho and rang to be hoisted up. Twenty feet, forty feet, they slowly went up to the 2200 and came down bit by bit. Hale leaned out with his carbide lantern, the pale light shining on the scramble of cable, broken pipes, and twisted metal. Below the 24, endless tangles were crammed into the narrow pump compartment and the edge of the chippy shaft.

Hale looked at Bolitho and the other men and he shrugged his shoulders in defeat. They checked the signal bells and turned the electricity on and off, "Bells and lights are working," said Hale.

"Can't do any more. We're going to have to leave this for the shaftmen and foreman, and come back tomorrow."

"Well, it sure ain't going anywhere now," said Bolitho.

Expecting to get chewed out by both Sullau and Braly, they rang the hoist engineer.

CHAPTER FIVE

FIRE IN THE SHAFT

It was late twilight on top of the hill. Arc lights shone down from the idler towers and a string of electric bulbs hung over the shaft collar. The harsh edges of artificial light filled the evening shadows as men worked under the headframe. A crew wrestled with the ten-foot reel for the electric cable, rolling it over next to the train tracks. Two of them had unbolted the sheave wheel at the pump compartment. Topman Barnicoat directed a group of men wrestling timber to be lowered.

The electricians came up to the surface at nine-thirty and Hale looked for Ernest Sullau the night boss, thinking, *He's going to have my ass.*

Sullau waited with concern. He motioned for Hale to come over. Hale dismissed Bolitho and the other men who had been with them, "Get on home, I'll take care of this," and followed Sullau. They stepped away from the headframe.

"I got a message that the cable dropped in the shaft," said Sullau.

"Yes Sir, it did."

"What happened?"

"I went up the shaft to get the twists out of her, taking the lower ties out. And we weren't there but a few minutes, and she started slipping. Man below yelled, and we made for the station, and down she come just as we got out of the shaft."

"You've done this plenty of times, what..."

"Sir, frankly, I can't imagine. We didn't do anything different from usual."

"Cable okay?"

Hale said slowly, "Well, probably not."

"Where is it?"

"Top is just below the 24 station. She's blocking the pump shaft and part of the chippy shaft. Who knows where the rest is. Down to the 2600 at least."

"We're going to need an electrician, can you...."

Hale broke in shaking his head, "We been on for eighteen hours. I ain't good for nothing now."

"What about the water? The other cables?"

"Looked like the water pipes was broken between the 22 and 24, maybe lower too. Air pipes loose, brackets tore off, but seemed okay."

"The signal bells?"

"Them are working, we checked, and called the hoist engineer. The electricity is on."

Sullau rubbed his forehead, "Okay, you head home with your men for the night, we'll take it from here."

He went into the office, greeted the timekeeper O'Keefe, and phoned the Speculator's shaft collar, "Send some men over here, a couple shaftmen, ropemen. I need help down on the 2400." Setting the receiver down he muttered, "What a mess..." and in meticulous letters, wrote a message to manager Braly.

Norman: Cable fell in shaft. Blocking chippy below 2400. Going down to pull it out. Will get water pipes working and the drills back on.

He was about to send word to Collins, the shift boss on the 3000, when Collins himself came through the door, "Been looking for you, Boss. Cable took out the water pipes. I pulled the drillers below the 3000 for the night. That okay?"

Sullau nodded, "Let them go. Shouldn't drill without water."

"Yeah, but there's still two men down on the 32. They wanted to prep work for tomorrow, so I let them stay."

Sullau gestured for Collins to follow him, "John, I'm going to need your help." They walked over to the shaft and Sullau said to Barnicoat, the topman, "Electrician told me the cable's in the way, blocking the shaft. I got a team coming, we'll haul it out."

"Okay, anything you need, just let me know," said Barnicoat.

The men from the Speculator showed up as Collins' drilling teams came out of the cages, looking annoyed at missing work.

"I'll explain it to Braly," Sullau told the drillers. "We'll have it fixed by tomorrow so you won't lose pay."

"Okay Joe, we're going down," he said to Barnicoat. Barnicoat rang the hoist engineer, *two bells, one bell, two bells,* "all clear," and the level.

The shaft team stepped into the cage and rang the hoist engineer, dropping into the shaft to the 2400. After a few minutes descending came the familiar press of weight as the cage slowed and dangled, they racked back the metal door.

Four men were already at the 24 station. Station tenders Conroy and Sheridan had heard the cable's crashing fall and lowered on the chippy cage from the 22. They stood chatting as Sullau and Collins arrived at the station.

"What about the blacksmith and the ore pocket?" asked Conroy. "There's nobody at the station."

Sheridan waved it off, "He can take care of himself, we got to help Sullau with this. Hey boss," he greeted Sullau. "Thought you'd need some help."

Cobb, the motorman from the north country and his swamper Fowler, had just dumped a load into the ore pockets and sat on their motor outside the turnsheets, eating lunch and watching the other men. "Boy, they got a problem," said Cobb.

Leaning into the pump compartment, Sullau peered down, "Can't see a damn thing." He stepped back into the chippy cage and pulled the signal rope in the shaft, two quick bells for *lower.* Rattling down the guides, the cage dropped forty feet farther and he rang the bells to stop between levels, surrounded by the timber scaffolding and rock walls of the shaft.

Drawing back the doors as wide as they would go, he squeezed his tree-trunk body between the timbers and the steel edge of the cage. Collins, wiry and lean, slipped out the other side. Both men held onto the top of the cage and stepped onto the cross-timbers in the adjacent pump shaft, holding on with 600 feet of shaft below them partly plugged with a mass of armored cable.

They felt the cool draft coming down the shaft from the surface, bringing fresh air, tempering the natural heat of the rock. This deep in the mine, the rock temperature was 90 degrees, the air moist and hot. Holding up his carbide lantern, Sullau peered down and fought back twinges of fear, standing exposed to the open shaft.

"Can't say I like hanging here," Collins said.

"Yeah, but this mess has got to come out."

With one foot on the timber below and the other propped on the dusty wall plate, Sullau held onto the gritty timber near his head and inspected the cable. His lantern's light fell onto the snarl and all he could see were tight loops crossed and twisted. There was no end to the cable in sight.

The compartment was narrow enough he could step across it if he stretched, but he didn't have the nerve. Instead, he sidled inch-by-inch. Brackets and clamps had been bent out by the falling cable. Water from the broken pipes dribbled down the active electrical lines, some of them with their outer sheaths torn. *Hale said the electricity was still on. Don't want to be electrocuted*, he thought grimly.

When he moved, he couldn't see his footing or judge the tangle of cable, and sharp little blades of anxiety pricked his gut. Balancing carefully and using both hands, he bent out a bracket to fit two fingers around it. Clapping a big hand over the crosspieces, he tried to get a solid hold on the timbers, but flecks of wood peeled off and rock dust stuck to his palms.

Below him, the fallen cable had large sections of the lead armor peeled open, exposing torn shreds and tufts of the insulation, hiding where the end might be.

"Christ, it's done for," he muttered. "Hale's lucky this didn't kill him."

He took a deep breath, lowered himself into the first coils, clinging with both hands, feet searching for the next timber down. Bracing his foot against the wall, he hunted for the cable's end amidst the bent and broken water pipes, electric lines, and hoses. *If I can just find the end, we can get a chain on the hoist rope and haul it out of here.*

The light from his lantern played across the shaft compartment, projecting shadows of the cable's looping tangles. Broken sections of pipe and fire sprinklers dangled, ripped loose by the whipping fall of the three-ton cable. Collins clung to the timbers on the opposite side of the pump compartment five feet away, looking ruefully, "Boss, this could set us back days."

He watched Sullau clambering down looking for the end of the cable, the foreman's lantern cupped in his huge hand. Collins called over, "Watch your lamp. Keep it away from the torn insulation."

"Yeah, I know."

They were below the cage now and the chippy shaft yawned at Sullau's side, disappearing into the darkness, while the cable's top loops hung on the cross-timbers of the pump compartment in front of him. Little spikes spread from his gut, stabbing the underside of his arms. His mouth was dry as he balanced, holding on with one hand and trying to find a place to put the lantern.

"Looks like a meat shredder down there."

"I ain't planning to jump," came Collins' reply.

If he lost balance forward he would tumble into the mangled cable. If he fell backward, it would be all the way down. He didn't dare hold onto the cable or cracked pipes, but hooked one arm around the tops of the timbers. Concentrating on each movement, he gripped the shaft trusses firmly, then bent to place his boot on a lower timber. The spacing was awkward, the timbers a little too wide, so he had to stretch to make each move, extending his leg out over the dark hole and feeling for a secure foothold. He moved slowly downward, tamping down his anxiety, each move careful and deliberate.

Around him, loops bent at sharp angles, frayed insulation hung on bent steel brackets and sprinkler heads. The last water trickled from the broken pipes.

With his lamp, he pushed on several loops of the cable to make a place for his hand. Some of the shredded insulation bent into the carbide flame, and with a soft *pfhsst*, it curled and burned brightly in a little puff of smoke. Sullau saw the flare and felt a jolt of alarm.

Below him there was a curved section of the cable with a broken end. He leaned forward thinking, *That's the end*, and reached down with the lantern to see better. It hit a loop, knocking its reflector against bare insulation. There was a little rush and hiss. Flame leapt from the lamp into the shredded insulation, and with a pop, it flared and lit the shaft.

He quickly set the lantern on the cross timber, hanging on with one hand and beat the flame with his free hand. With a few big slaps, he smashed it out and only a curling wisp of smoke was left. Then behind him, another flame burst out. He twisted around, slapping at it, but it did not stop. With each strike of his palm, the flames from the burning insulation leapt into other coils.

He yelled to Collins, "John, I got my lamp too close!"

"What?" Collins looked over his shoulder just as flames popped across the shaft. Burning pieces fell into the torn and ragged cable below. Collins jumped sideways, one hand on the timber above, and hurriedly beat at the flames. He tried to smother them with his hands and stomped on the ones below him against the timbers. The flames darted from loop to loop and burst out all around them.

"Oh my God…" The realization came to Sullau of what he had just unleashed.

"Fire in the shaft!"

Collins and Sullau were suddenly encircled. Flames ran up the thin boards protecting the bell wires and the telephone line, crackling and giving off gusts of black smoke.

"Climb out Sullau!"

They yelled up the shaft to the other men. "Water! Get water!"

They scrambled through spreading flames into the chippy cage, frantically rang, and were hoisted up to the station with the fire at their feet.

Fowler ripped off the top of a ten-gallon drinking keg and poured it down the shaft. They wheeled a fifty gallon barrel of water to the edge and Conroy and Sheridan helped spray it down. The water struck the flames and hissed, then the fire shot up as if untouched.

Cobb grabbed the water pipe and turned the stopcock. Nothing. The pipes were broken. A few barrels was all they had.

"For God's sake, get the men out, get them out!" yelled Sullau.

He turned to Collins, "Hoist up! Tell them up top!"

Collins jumped in the cage with Sheridan and Conway, rang for the hoist, nine bells for *danger*, one for *up*. Within a few seconds the cage started toward the surface, half a mile above.

The shaft filled with flames and flying cinders, heat pressed into Sullau's face and forced him back. The crackling became a deep whirr, like the sound of thickly flying wings. The electric bulbs went out, and a gloom engulfed the men, as flames in the shaft threw pulses of light through billowing smoke.

"Surface don't know till Collins gets up!" Sullau turned and yelled to Cobb and Fowler, "I'm going to the Spec side. Go north, tell shifter Bronson to meet me at the B switch. Run!"

Cobb and Fowler nodded and ran off down the crosscut heading northeast.

Sullau yelled after them. "Check every stope, every drift! Get them all!" Cobb waved back with the lantern and they disappeared.

Sullau glanced at the shaft. *What have I done?*

His chest tightened and he wiped his eyes. There were more than four hundred men down here. His men.

He paused and his head bent slightly forward, "Lord, please help ..." Then he turned his back on the station and ran south toward the Speculator.

64

CHAPTER SIX

A Geyser of Flame

At midnight, Barnicoat stood at the headframe of the Granite Mountain, tallying the skips of ore and overseeing the traffic in and out of the shaft. The topman leaned on a metal girder talking to the mine's fireman Angus McLeod and yardman George Lapp, who pinched a fresh wad of tobacco from a bag and tucked it in his lip.

Barnicoat wrinkled his nose looking at the other man's teeth, "Filthy habit, George."

"Pfah, don't look at it if you don't like it."

A skip loaded with ore lifted out of the shaft. The men on the other side of the frame unlocked it and released the bottom gate, dumping the ore into the bins behind the headframe.

Barnicoat made a chalk mark for the load on the board next to the shaft, and noticed the cable to the chippy cage was coming up. "Hope that's Sullau. We need that mess out of the pump and chippy shaft. Haven't heard a damn thing from him."

"Cable must have gone down hard," Lapp said.

"Hale said it were a mess. Ripped everything loose. Broke the water pipes. Collins sent home all his drillers below 3000."

"There goes a day's pay for them."

Barnicoat cocked his head, sniffed the air a few times, and asked, "Where's that smell coming from?"

Before Lapp could answer, the cage carrying Collins, Conroy and Sheridan came rattling up from below. As soon as it reached the collar, Collins yelled to the topman and station tender, "Fire on the 24!"

He slammed the cage doors opened and bounded out, "Change over the skips to the cages, we got to get the men up!"

Sheridan and Conroy helped unhitch the ore skip and switch over the stack of cages, swinging a few feet above the shaft. Barnicoat leaned over, holding onto the steel crossbar and looking down into the black abyss, "That cage that just come up, it smells gassy Pete."

65

Conroy and Sheridan paid no attention. They rolled the skip onto the crossover rails under the headframe, got the cage stack into place over the shaft collar, and bolted it into the top connecter.

A faint odor of burning tar now rose out of the shaft. Sheridan looked up, alarmed.

"Goddamn! Sullau's down there with the whole shift!"

Conroy hit the side of the cage, "I'm going down. We'll get the men ready to hoist."

Collins insisted, "No! Signal bells will go out with the squawker. You ain't going be able to ring us."

Conroy turned to Collins, "If the men on the 22 can't ring, they ain't getting hoisted. They're trapped."

"Let me talk to the engineer," Conroy picked up the phone and rang the engine house. He plugged his ear to block the noise around them, then yelled into the receiver, "Evans, there's fire down in the shaft, we got to hoist the men!" He shouted louder, "We got to hoist them!" The skip and cages clanged deafeningly. Conroy held up the phone in anger and waved it, "The hell of it. He can't hear me."

Sheridan grabbed the mouthpiece out of his hand and slammed it down on the phone cradle. "Just ring him the damn level. We're headed to the 22."

Alarmed, Collins insisted, "No Pete, the bells probably ain't working."

Sheridan brushed him off, "The hell. We'll go to the 22 and check the squawker. And get a bunch of them out."

"Hold on, let me go talk to the hoist engineer, so he knows what's going on." Collins ran toward the hoist house, nearly two hundred yards away, dodging between the stacks of timber, making his way under the five sets of huge idler towers that held up the cable.

As soon as Collins turned his back, Sheridan and Conroy jumped on the stacked cages.

"What're you doing?" Barnicoat demanded.

"Going to the 22."

"Collins said no."

66

"Hell with him. He's shifter for the 3000. He got no say about the 22. Them's our men."

The hanging cages swayed slightly and Barnicoat put his hand on the corner. "I'm the topman. Wait until Collins talks with the hoist engineer."

Sheridan yelled, "Joe, there's forty men on the 2200 in the north country!"

"I know..."

"Moore and all his boys in the south! We're getting them. Stand back." Sheridan rang the hoist engineer to lower.

Barnicoat paused, the black hole of the shaft gaping a step away, the burnt odor growing stronger.

"Pete..."

Sheridan paid no attention. He stood in the cage, rang again and barked at the signal bells, "Come on Evans, get to it! We got no time!"

In the engine house Evans sat in his high backed chair, the top button of his shirt loose, big levers in front of him, running the hoist engine and the two thick drums of cable that were attached to the cages and ore skips. He slowly chewed on a cigar, and spat into the bucket at his feet. He had just hung up the phone, unable to hear the men at the shaft collar.

"What were they on about?" he asked himself, "Fire?" The hum of the generators and the idled 4000 horsepower hoist engine filled the room, and a low hiss of steam came from the heating pipes. The bells mounted just in front of him rang, and he listened to the pattern, *six bells*, pause, *two bells*, it repeated again almost without a break, then *two bells* for lower, and then the whole pattern a third time, even faster. He said to himself, "They sure want the 22."

At the cage, Sheridan rang impatiently again and again, pulling *two bells* for *lower* and *six* pause *two* again, screaming at the signal box, "Goddamn it Evans, drop us already!"

Conroy cranked the phone line and shouted into the receiver. Evans had to hold the phone away from his head, all he heard was, "Let us down!"

Shaking his head, Evans released the brakes and started

dropping the stacked cage down the shaft, muttering, "I don't like this..." but let it continue.

The cable spooled smoothly off the huge drum of the hoist, through the small window and lifted tightly over the wheels of the five idler towers to the very apex of the headframe one hundred sixty feet above the yard. There, it glided silently over the spinning twelve-foot sheave wheel and straight down into the shaft, guiding the stacked cage with Conroy and Sheridan on it, descending to the 2200.

Collins burst in the door and yelled, "Evans, we got fire at the 2400. Hell's bustin' loose down there."

"I just lowered a cage to the 22."

"Goddamn that Conroy," cursed Collins, looking at the big round dial that showed the cage levels.

"What you saying, John?"

"Bring them back up."

"Can't, they ain't rung me."

"Do the bells work?"

"What do you mean?" Evans asked in disbelief. "They better work."

"Fire was setting to run, it may have taken them out. Bring that cage up."

"Well, I ain't heard nothing."

"How about the squawker?"

"Nope. What's going on?"

Collins cursed, "I should have talked them out of going down." He looked at the big wheel marking the level, "If you hear anything from them, get them up, quick as you can," then he started out of the engine room and headed back toward the shaft, now shrouded by upwelling smoke. When he got near the collar, all the men working under the headframe had backed away and were standing in the yard. He found Lapp and McLeod.

"The power in the shaft just went out. Nothing's ringing. No bells from any level, not the squawker either," said Lapp to Collins. "Barnicoat left to find the night electrician at the Spec."

"Jesus," said Collins.

A skip tender flung open the door to the hoist house, yelling to Evans, "Smoke's heavy at the headframe, you got to get those boys back up!"

"They're parked at 2200," said Evans. "Can't move the cage until they tell me it's clear. Cut somebody in half if they're loading men."

The other man insisted, "Something's wrong Evans."

He looked again at the clock. *They should have rung to come up.* The powerful hum of the hoist engine resonated in the men's guts. Evan's hands trembled slightly, ready to spring to action. Through the open door, he could hear men shouting outside.

Damn... he thought.

Another minute went by and no signal bells sounded. No hint came from below. He jiggled the throttle, knowing it would shake the cage up and down a few inches. No answer.

Suddenly he knew, *Fire's burned out the bells. They can't ring. They're trapped.*

He pulled the brake, jammed the throttle forward, and the engine woke. It accelerated and within seconds the big drums were reeling in the half-mile of steel cable at man speed, pulling up the cage far below. A ripple of fear flashed through Evans and he shoved the throttle faster, to ore speed.

He felt the pulse of energy through the levers. Before him in the cavernous room, the drums rolled, each cylinder as large as a locomotive. He reached to his right and threw the knife switch, disconnecting the fail safe and increasing the speed yet again.

The pitch rose and the big dial swept through the levels, *1000, 900, 800....*

"Bring them up safe," he said under his breath.

With the fail safe off, if he did not time his brake right, the cage would pull right through the headframe and over the top of the sheave wheels. He would kill them.

His eyes riveted on the drums' flange, watching the chalk marks flash by, *300, 200, 100, ...* Evans yanked the throttle back and shoved the brake lever forward.

The cage shot up out of the shaft collar in a flaming geyser, and a surge of heat swept through the yard. Men threw their arms in front of their faces as fire roared upward through the skeleton of the head frame.

In the center of the fire, ten feet above the ground swung the cage, glowing red hot. Inside were two forms, Conroy and Sheridan, charred black, clutching onto each other in a death embrace.

Everyone across the yard stiffened in shock, transfixed with horror. "Oh my God," murmured a station tender and shut his eyes.

The chippy hoist engineer came out and yelled, "Get them down!"

Below the headframe, McCleod and Lapp sprayed the cage with hoses until they could get close. With heavy leather gloves on, they opened the cage and fought tears as they lifted the blackened remains out. The arms wrapped around each other, feet and hands burned away. An arm broke off and fell. The gaping crisp of their friend's skull wobbled, hairless, all its skin and muscle burnt around the hollow eye sockets.

They moved the bodies near the hoist house and wrapped them in a canvas sheet. Lapp came back to pick up the fallen arm and tuck it into the bundle. He stepped back from the lifeless forms that used to be his friends, leaned against the angle iron, and dropped his head.

Men stood motionless across the mineyard, staring at the breath of hell rising from the shaft before them.

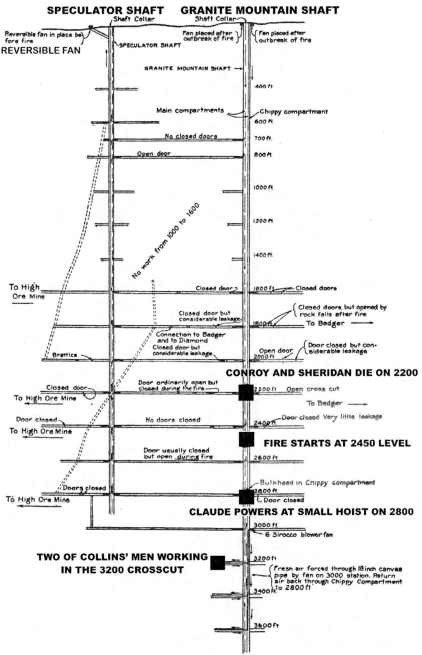

FIGURE 2.—Section of Granite Mountain shaft.

Schematic layout of Granite Mountain and Speculator shafts

71

CHAPTER SEVEN

SMOKE ON THE 2000

As Moore neared the top of the ladders of stope 2218, he stopped for an instant, raised his face and sniffed the air. A jab of anxiety cut through him as he quickly stepped into the drift and saw haze, clenched his lamp, and looked down the tunnel. He remembered the smoke from the fire six weeks before.

It can't be the Modoc. The High Ore closed those tunnels. Is something burning in Goodell's beat?

He ran down the drift toward the Speculator and stopped at the opening to stope 17, Goodell's first manway, but as he ran the air cleared.

What the hell? He turned back to his manway, agitated and determined, *Where's this coming from?*

Charging northward toward the Granite Mountain, the smoke got worse and filled the drift, and his fear grew. He kept running, smoke thicker and thicker until it was so bad he had to turn around.

He knew the smell. When wood burned without enough oxygen it made carbon monoxide, wood gas. The killer. It was the worst gas in mine fires, stealing into a man's blood, making his veins cherry red as he suffocated from the inside.

He ticked off possibilities, *Fire in the north stopes? In the Granite Mountain? Makes no sense*, he thought. *We got the best shaft on the hill…*

He quickly thought through the connections, *Where's safe? Spec shaft ain't running.*
Go to the Diamond 1800? No, it's too far.
Down to the 22, out the High Ore…

He ran back to the 17, then the 18 stopes and shouted down each manway, "Fire! Gas coming! Head to the High Ore!"

At the 18 stope, he swung down the ladder until he reached the group of new men and shouted, "There's a fire. Climb down to the 22!"

The men looked at him, "Ain't we going to get hoisted?"

"2000 is blocked. Can't get to the station. Head to the High Ore. Tell everyone below. Climb down, then south. Do it!"

He raced back up the ladders thinking, *Now, get the boys in the 48 stope.*

He got to the top and stepped onto the 2000 sill. Smoke had already rolled in. He held his breath and dove into the choking murk, running north along the drift. His thoughts flashed, listing the men working on the far side of his beat, past the crosscut to the Granite Mountain station. *I got nine boys in the mid-floors. Eight more down on the 2200 sill, the motorman, drillers and muckers, the guys in the short drifts, the hot crosscut.*

My God, why is this smoke here? I got to get the crews out!

His lamp dimmed, and almost went out in the swirling gloom but he knew the route, feeling his hand along the rough broken wall, eyes closed against the smoke's harsh bite. Stumbling on the uneven side of the track, his mind clicked through options, making a plan. *We're so far back in here. Can we get ahead of the smoke down on the 22? Then come back across to the Spec and out the High Ore?*

He gasped, sucking hot smoke that burned deep in his lungs and fought not to choke. Under his foot there was the point of a moveable rail, *I'm at the crosscut switch.* He went past four timber sets and the hot press of smoke suddenly lessened, and he broke into clearer air. The lamp's flame flared.

Damn, is it coming from the Granite Mountain? he asked himself, bewildered.

He kept running, going a hundred yards, past three short drifts, and reached the manway into the 48 stope. Men from the stope were already coming off the ladder and onto the sill. Truax and Erikson were in the lead, their faces frightened.

Moore yelled, "Turn around! Go down to the 22! We can't get out on the 2000!"

They stared at him and he pushed past, "Follow me. Grab all the men you can."

He yelled down the ladder into the dark. "This is Moore, get the hell out of the way!" There were several lamps below in the

73

narrow vertical hole, illuminating men's hands and faces. "Gas is coming, head back down!"

His boots met the mucker Knutti midway down the ladder and almost stripped him off. He scampered past yelling, "Get to the 22!" pivoted and climbed down another floor.

Sullivan was below him, "Stand aside!" Moore shouted down between his feet. He slid down half the next ladder, jumped the last crosspieces, landed heavily on the floor. He grabbed Sullivan's shoulder, spun him around and pushed him head first toward the ladder, yelling "To the 22!"

The call relayed down through the floors to the other men below, Laszkeics and John Lisa. On a lower landing, Garrity and Marthey stood, "Don't we hoist at the Granite 2000?"

Moore brushed them off, "No! Gas is coming from there. Follow me fast as you can!"

He swung down the ladders one to the next, level by level. The skin on his hands ripped against the rough-cut boards as he passed the men, urging them all to follow. He had a single consuming thought, *we got to outrun it on the 22*.

CHAPTER EIGHT

FOREARMS AND KNEES

Moore's call echoed through the floors and the men on the upper floors climbed down, relaying the alarm. Men dropped their tools and crowded onto the ladders in chaos.

"Let's get out of here!" shouted Wynder to his partners Roberts and Voko.

They climbed down, jostling with men from the other floors. It took only a minute to get to the sill. Roberts and Voko followed Wynder and they ran up the drift toward the main crosscut, straight toward the Granite Mountain.

Wynder shouted over his shoulder, "They'll hoist us up!"

Voko was a big man with long legs and arms, ill-fit into the awkward narrow tunnels. He tripped several times and fell behind as he tripped over the blocky ties and tracks.

They turned right at the main crosscut, with six hundred feet to the station. Wynder held up his lantern to look ahead and stopped. A flood of smoke black as night filled the tunnel, churning toward them.

Three other men shoved him out of the way as they passed, diving toward the station and the only escape they could imagine, the Granite Mountain shaft.

Wynder hesitated, then followed the three with Voko behind him, Roberts and other men on their heels. "Keep going!" Wynder screamed.

They were engulfed, the air blacker and more terrible each step and their lamps went out. Noxious gusts raked their lungs. They dropped to the floor and began crawling along the rails on their forearms and knees, noses against the gritty cool steel to sip the last of the air.

In the panic, everyone crawled in the same direction. As the smoke became intolerable, Wynder thought, *This is wrong, we're going to die...* He made a quick decision and screamed, "Turn around!"

Voko was at Wynder's side, floundering in the blackness. He couldn't breath, "I'm dying!" he cried. Wynder punched him in the face, screaming, "Turn around!" and dragged him back the other way.

They began crawling the opposite direction. Within a few yards, they ran head-on into Roberts and others from the stope, still scuttling like half-poisoned rats toward the Granite Mountain shaft. The men tangled on the tracks, unable to see or breathe, clutching and tearing at each other in animal desperation.

Wynder shouted, "It's me! It's me!" but Roberts shouldered past him and forced Voko face down, crawling over the top of him, and disappeared into the smoke, leaving the other man lying stunned. Wynder reached over and pulled Voko forward again, away from the station, and they crawled until they cleared the edge of the smoke. He lurched to his feet and helped Voko up, then lit a candle so they could see where to go.

"Run," he gasped to Voko.

They threw a quick shuddering glance behind them, and headed southward along the 2202 drift toward the Speculator shaft and the distant connection to the High Ore.

CHAPTER NINE

MOORE INTO THE 2254

The alarm could only travel as fast as a man could run in the dark. A miner heard the relay of Moore's yells in stope 18 and ran toward the northern end of the Edith May 2200 to warn the others. He stopped at the bottom of manway 17 and turned off the compressed air to quiet the drills, then beat on the pipe with the butt of his knife. The metallic blows rang out and he yelled into the stope, "Fire!"

Northwest along the Edith May, nobody had heard any warnings. Noise and dust swirled from the usual work. Crews in the short drifts drilled the middle holes preparing to shoot a round. Carpenters in the hot 2254 crosscut worked on the trolley boxes. The drillers near the end of the crosscut replaced a six-foot drill bit. It seemed like a normal night on the 2200.

Then loud shouts echoed through the 2202 drift, "Fire!"

The warning relayed along the tunnel from crew to crew. Drills fell silent. Men looked at each other, the focus of their work suddenly shaken, a confused pause as they tried to understand.

Then another shout from a man running by, urgent and frightened, "Get to the shaft!" Drillers in the short drifts and runs left their machines and ran, timbermen and carpenters tossed their tools aside, sprinting south toward the main crosscut. A man from stope 18 called to them, "Come this way! To the Speculator shaft!" Lamps appeared out of the side drifts, multiplied, carried by dark shadows running, heavy footfalls grating, and sounds of frightened breaths.

At the farthest end of the drift, the swamper had just hitched the last loaded car, and the motortrain was ready to return. The swamper heard the warning yells and the motorman shouted, "Come on!" They leapt off the engine and fled, leaving the motor with its train of ten filled cars sitting on the rails. Coming down the tracks, they stopped for a frantic moment at the entrance to the hot 2254 crosscut, shouting over the noise of the fan, "Run for the shaft!" then set off past the 48 manway toward the Granite Mountain crosscut.

The motorman led the swamper as they turned into the main crosscut, out of which Wynder and Voko had just crawled a mere minute before. They dashed toward the station, straight into the smoke pouring from the shaft. Bewildered, the swamper dropped his lamp and collapsed. Another thirty feet and the motorman fell, struggling on his knees with his last strength, then unconscious.

The smoke rolled over them silently, then out of the crosscut into the main Edith May drifts, slipping north and south into every niche and opening.

The last men appeared from the farther reaches of the Edith May drifts. The three drillers who had been working far back in the hot 2254 crosscut heard the yells of the motorman and swamper. They emerged from the long crosscut and veered around the loaded ore car. Their only thought was to get hoisted to safety. They ran and passed the manway to the 48 stope. Six floors above them, Moore and his men rumbled down the ladders.

Running into one of the parallel drifts toward the station, the drillers rounded a corner and crumpled to the ground, overwhelmed by the poisonous gas.

After climbing over Wynder and Voko, the contract miner Roberts and other men reached the station. For a few short seconds, they cowered in the hot caustic murk pumping from the shaft, screaming and unable to understand. Thirty feet from them, Conroy and Sheridan embraced each other as they hung helplessly in the chippy cage in the shaft.

The station erupted in a torrent of flames and another pulse of smoke pressed up the shaft and outward along the crosscut. In a few minutes men across the Edith May were cut down. Only the smoke prowled the lifeless drifts, pushing toward the last refuges of air in the far northwest where Moore and his men were.

Moore swung down the ladder into the lower floors, "Down! Down! We'll break for the Spec!"

The wooden rungs creaked and edges splintered under the stomping feet. Then, ten breathless and tense men spilled out of the 48 manway onto the 22 sill, a minute after the motorman and swamper and the drilling crew from the 2254 crosscut fled by. Moore was in front, Marthey and Knutti right behind, the others at their heels.

The drift was eerily quiet. "Wait here," said Moore and ran down the tunnel, asking himself, *Can we get past the 2275 crosscut over to the Spec?* He ducked into each short run, searching and yelling for men. *Is there anyone left?* he wondered.

Back at the opening of the 48 manway, the group threw frantic looks around them and Truax demanded, "What the hell we standing here for?"

"Moore said to wait," yelled Garrity.

"Bullshit! I'm going to the Granite Mountain!" Truax rushed southward down the drift toward the main crosscut. Sullivan followed and their lights bobbed away into the dark.

Marthey and Garrity watched in panic as the two ran away, while Lisa and four others nervously paced, ready to run.

Following the tracks, Sullivan and Truax entered a maze of short drifts and laterals with rail switches, and ran directly into the fumes slowly flooding the tunnels.

"Back, back!" Truax yelled, and they both retreated, reaching the switch near the manway. They could see Garrity's lamp and made toward it.

Moore was farther along the drift, searching the last of the short runs, making sure he found any of his men that were still there. *We're the last*, he thought.

Nausea started overwhelming him, he had been in the gas too long. In his lamplight, all around him the haze was dense and foreboding. Smoke and gas had come into the 22 just like the 20, rolling into all the drifts. He called one last time but nobody answered, then turned and fled back where he had left his crew.

Possibilities shot through his mind – distances, drifts, and air. *The smoke's spread through the Edith May, every drift, from here to the Speculator.* His face was a cascade of emotion, *We can't make the High Ore. We're cut off.*

There was one choice or death. *Bulkhead. The 2254.*

The gas was bad and it took all his concentration to get back. Truax and the others had returned, standing anxiously in the growing haze, ready to bolt like horses in a thunderstorm. Moore shouted to them, "Back into the 54 crosscut, on the left!"

Sullivan and Erikson, their faces agitated, screamed and pressed forward, "We got to run for the Speculator!"

"No!" yelled Moore, and yanked Erikson around, shoving him in the opposite direction, deeper into the drift.

Erikson resisted, trying to push by, and Moore drove his shoulder into the man's chest. He tried to break free but Moore shook him mercilessly, "You're going to die if you don't listen. We're bulkheading."

Face wide with panic the man pleaded, "Nay! Not bury meself."

Spring-tight, Moore slammed Erikson into wall and cocked both fists, ready to swing, eyes burning a hole in the bigger man. "You're going to do what I say."

Moore turned to the rest, "If you want to die, run there," pointing toward the Granite Mountain station.

"You want to live, follow me."

Marthey froze with fear, "How we getting out?"

Moore yanked his arm, "Run, dammit!"

The smoke was already around them. "Get all the water you can find, drag what timber you see."

He pointed, "Into the 2254. Tunnel on the left at the fan."

Shadows of legs and torsos jogged along the walls in the lamplight, sprinting northwest, racing for their lives. Fragmented questions went through Moore's mind, *Can I save them? Do we have time?*

In front of them the drift split, "To the fan. Turn left!"

He held his lantern up and saw smoke keeping pace with them, curling around the timbers. *We're not outrunning it...*

In the opening of the crosscut, timbers were stacked between the wall and the rails, a pile of lagging, tools all along the sides.

"Quick now! Boards, nails, tools," ordered Moore. Lisa pulled a set of the six-foot long boards from the pile on the floor, and heaved it across his shoulder. The remaining pile fell over and boards scattered across the rails, into the tunnel and against the single loaded ore car on the tracks. Laszkeics grabbed more off the ground.

Marthey snatched up two canvas bags of nails, and cursed as one split apart, spilling across the boards and tracks. He bent down to pick up a handful, Moore yelled, "Leave it! Take the one bag!" Moore seized two hammers, a saw, a sack of wooden wedges. Other men seized shovels and empty dynamite boxes.

"Bring three of those sprags!" Moore pointed to the posts leaning against the wall. The crisp orders focused the men, steadying them in the frantic chaos.

A Leyner drill leaned against the wall of the crosscut, and two-inch compressor pipe was on the floor, the hose spooled off the drill into the darkness of the crosscut.

Moore pointed at the drill. "Get the submarine."

Garrity stood flustered, "The what?"

"The drill's water tank. Get it."

He intended to put the bulkhead close to the entrance of the crosscut, but the smoke was already around them.

He made a quick decision, "Go in another hundred feet!" he ordered.

The men carried everything they could, past the loaded ore car, ventilation fan, and its canvas piping running along the roof of the tunnel.

A hundred more feet, the smoke still rolled around them. *Damn*, Moore cursed again to himself, "Farther!" he shouted.

Another dozen yards, Moore flicked out his knife, stuck it into the canvas piping hanging from the timbers. Deftly, he cut it in a circle around the outside, tore the remaining canvas off of it for fifty feet. Then he cut the section free and stuffed the wad under his arm, leaving a long line of wire hangers, bent and hanging, half-ripped out of the upper cross timbers.

The air became hotter as they went, all were heaving deep breaths in the thick hot tunnel. Seconds ticked by as they rushed down the crosscut with quick muttered curses.

"Keep going! Outrun the gas, get into good air!"

81

Moore held up a lamp, but the men could not see the floor. Laszkeics fell, dropping his boards. Moore threw down his load, shoving the boards back onto the other man's shoulder.

Overhead was more canvas fanpipe. Moore stripped another section with his knife, stuffed it under his arm and picked up the tools.

His mind raced ahead, but each time he started to yell for them to stop and build the bulkhead, he realized, *It's coming too fast. Smoke's already here…*

Moore knew they were getting close to the end of the tunnel, *We're running out of room. There won't be enough space. Not enough air.*

Calculating, deciding, he saw a glint of light on metal just ahead. *A drill.* They were at the end of the crosscut. There was no other choice.

Now!

Moore stopped abruptly, "Build a brattice here!"

Truax and Sullivan tried to fit the lagging boards across the tunnel and Moore shouted, "No, it's too wide," he said, "Posts across the bottom, on the rails. Put the lagging upright, nail it into the timber set."

He heard the hiss of the air hose from the drill behind them. "Get the air hose off that drill!" he shouted to Garrity, who was handing Lisa and Sullivan boards. Garrity ran to the back wall, struggled with the threaded nut but could not release it.

"I can't get it off!"

Moore bounded over holding a hammer and slammed the edge of the spud nut, then hit the edge again, spinning it off and releasing the air hose from the drill.

"Help them," he said to Garrity, pointing at Sullivan and Erickson, who were nailing boards across the timbers.

He jammed the hose into Lisa's hands, "Take this! Keep the gas back!"

Lisa jumped over the side of the growing bulkhead, and pulled the hose in front of the posts they had nailed in, loose coils at his feet. Moore moved back to the construction, yelling, "Open it full! Keep the pressure even! Roof to floor, side to side, circle it!"

Lisa aimed the nozzle down the drift and the air hissed loudly in a powerful stream, almost wrenching the hose from his hands. Dust and dirt flew up from the floor, and the dark fumes boiled back. He swept the opening of the tunnel again and again.

They set posts across the bottom, nailed lagging boards to it upright against the timber set above, creating a frame. Moore split the canvas fan piping down the seam, and cut seven-foot lengths. Marthey and Sullivan spread the canvas across the lagging and nailed it tight.

"We're running out of lagging!" Lisa heard behind him.

"I'll get some," yelled Marthey. "It's just up the cut." He held his shirt sleeve over his mouth, running past the dome of clean air made by Lisa's hose and into a wall of warm smothering smoke, trying to get to a pile of lagging they had dropped. After only fifteen feet he started reeling, turned and staggered back.

He fell past Lisa. "Can't do it," he gasped between huffs, and leaned back against the wall. He rolled onto his knees and threw up, putting his forehead on the ground.

"You okay?"

There was no answer.

Moore looked at Marthey's dark figure lying at Lisa's feet and yelled to Lisa, "Valve open wide?

"Yes!"

Marthey rolled back onto his back, eyes closed and his face tight in a grimace. Moore jumped over the bottom of the bulkhead and grabbed Marthey, pulling him back behind, shouting to Lisa, "Keep that hose going! Hold the smoke back!"

Fear ran through Lisa, it took both hands to hold the hose as the compressed air shot out. He kept circling across the roof, timbered sets, and down along the walls and floor, across the middle, repeating.

Men pulled up mud from the wet back of the drift and brought it to the bulkhead, filling gaps with the sloppy concrete, building it up in steps from the floor.

"We're out of canvas! Give us your clothes!" Moore yelled over the blast of pressurized air. The men stripped, split their overalls and coats apart. Moore opened one of the crates and

83

poured the tainted copper water from a drill submarine, dumping in dirt and muck. They soaked the pieces of clothing in the thick muddy slurry and slapped them onto the boards where the canvas stopped, nailing them onto the face. Every hole was plugged with slime-covered fabric. Garrity and Laszkeics had only their socks on with big streaks of dirt across their chests and stomachs while they ladled mud onto the surface, Sullivan and Truax were totally nude, and Moore had only his boots.

He pounded a nail through a lagging board. The end split off and left a hole at eye-level. "Damn," he said through clenched teeth, and pulled off one of his boots, cut the soft leather top off with his knife, and spread it out against the boards on either side, nailing it to cover the hole. Garrity slapped mud over it to seal the edges.

The smoke slipped around the edges of the air blast, quickly and stealthily the instant the stream of pressurized air went past. Moore felt his dizziness increase and drove himself to think clearly. They were all breathing the same poisoned air. He pushed them harder, *There's no time, no time...* He glanced over at Garrity and Sullivan and could see the effects. Their shoulders and faces drooped with fatigue, a glazed look in their eyes, and fear stole through him. He knew what the gas was doing.

Quiet desperation seized the group, hope ebbing away. Moore's anger welled up, redoubling his effort. He took the lead in everything, reinforcing the base of the wall, and confidently slapped Garrity's shoulder, "Good work!" then turned to the others, "We'll have it soon."

The bulkhead took shape, and Moore left an opening in the side for Lisa to squeeze back through.

Moore's fear surfaced only once, erupting when Erickson misplaced a board and left a gap, "Don't do it like that!" he shouted, shoving Erickson aside. Wrenching the board loose, he sawed an inch off the end and reset it. Three hammer strokes snapped. Nails in, boards tight. He regained his composure and said with forced cool, "Like that."

Outside the rising bulkhead, Lisa tried to keep the smoke and gas back. It pressed against the stream of hissing air like an incoming tide, surging toward him whenever he turned the air hose another direction. He tried to cover all the open space evenly, but the dark wall crept closer, slipping along the ceiling and floor. The fumes became stronger, forcing him to step back another few inches toward the bulkhead.

Pounding of hammers echoed down the drift, the hollow clap of wood boards, clothes being ripped, and mud slopped into the cracks. Short clipped voices sounded as men fought for life with their backs against a wall of solid rock.

"Plaster mud along the sides! Fill the gaps!" The men slapped the mud onto the face, driving it in with their palms and fingers until it extruded through every opening, sealing the bulkhead air-tight.

"You almost got it?" Lisa called out. His voice trembled and his back was almost brushing the bulkhead.

"No!" yelled Moore between hammer strokes. "Shoot it toward the floor! Gas is sneaking under the smoke. I can taste it."

The last of the trolley boards were nailed. Their shirts and pants had been used to fill holes and caked with mud to make it airtight. Under constantly working hands, the bulkhead took its final shape.

"Bring in the hose!"

Lisa turned to the bulkhead, handed the hose in to Garrity and then jumped through the opening.

Without the restraining pressure, the smoke broke like a wave into the face of the wall. From inside, Garrity aimed the hose at the hole, keeping the pressure on. Moore set the last board in place. Lisa stripped himself, Moore split open the pants with his knife, and nailed the clothes over the lagging. Two men smothered the edges with mud, then stepped back.

Suddenly all they heard was the deafening hiss of the air hose. Moore stared at it, knowing the air was coming from the shaft. He quickly closed the valve. *If there is any gas in this hose, we're dead.*

With the compressed air shut off, stillness filled the chamber. A carbide lantern threw light on the men, dirt streaked and naked, eyes wild, chests heaving and falling.

They looked around at each other uncertainly, tools still in their hands, tense and aware of how small the space was for the ten of them. The bright little flame of the carbide lamp sang, barely audible, thin and high-pitched like a tiny plaintive cry.

Sitting down bare-assed, leaning against the gritty bulkhead, Moore let out a sigh of exhausted relief and thought, *We did it.*

Then he looked around at the men, each one in turn, and said, "Good work boys."

CHAPTER TEN

OUT TO THE BADGER

Sullau headed west to the Edith May switch, then turned into the main drift, his voice booming, "Fire! Follow me to the High Ore!" Men came out of the short drifts and down from the stopes, following his broad back and terse orders through the maze. By the time they made it to the Speculator station, the group was ten strong.

Frank Fiscus was at the station with the sampling team. He stood anxiously holding a bag of ore samples with his single arm, and at his feet were the team's sharp-ended geologist's hammers. The other two men searched for the bell cord at the shaft. Behind them huddled panicked days pay miners, Greeks and Serbs new to the mine.

Fiscus' frightened face showed in Sullau's lamp and he put down the bag of samples, "Mr. Sullau, they can't find the pull cord. How do we ring the hoist?"

"Can't, the cages aren't down this far. The shaft is being repaired."

The men by the shaft stopped searching, and their eyes widened with fear, "You mean we can't get out?"

"I'll show you. Stick close, we have to go south." Sullau turned to the group of new men and, motioning sharply, ordered "Come with me!" They looked at each other and crowded behind him as he led them down the crosscut, south toward the High Ore. Nineteen men hustled to keep up. After a hundred feet the tunnel split three ways.

"Go that way," he pointed to the middle branch. "It leads to the High Ore shaft, you can get hoisted from there."

Frightened and unsure, Fiscus said, "I don't know the route."

"Nor I," said another.

The other men gathered close, their eyes following Sullau's gestures.

He pointed again down the middle crosscut. "In six hundred feet there's an iron door. Go through it. Then the crosscut splits. Take the right, and there's a sign to the High Ore. Station's another thousand feet."

Sullau turned to go back, but Fiscus dropped the samples and grabbed his arm, "Are you crazy?" He stared at Sullau, "You'll die if you go back."

"There's men on the 26 we have to help. I left word for Bronson to wait for me."

"But..."

"Go!" and he shoved Fiscus on.

Sullau ran back toward the Speculator. Smoke was already coming from the shaft, seeping into the tunnels joining the Speculator and Granite Mountain. Reaching the station, he found a dozen men milling around, confused and frightened.

"Come here!" he commanded, and they circled around. On the ground, he smoothed the dirt with his boot, knelt down and flicked out his knife, then stabbed a hole, "We're right here."

With quick precise movements, he sliced a map of the tunnels leading to the High Ore. "Here's the main crosscut south, here's the ventilation door, here's where you turn right. There is a sign right here, and here's the High Ore shaft." He stood up. "You can make it. That's the crosscut you take," he said, pointing to the tunnel. "I have to help the men below. God be with you."

Alone, Sullau fought his way past the smoke and into the northern workings. At the B switch, he found Bronson, who yelled "Boss! Damn, I'm glad to see you. Cobb came through shouting about a fire in the shaft."

"We've got to get the men off the 26," said Sullau. "They have to climb out before the gas hits."

They both knew the 26 was an island. There were no outlets to any other mines, and now, the shafts were impassable. The only way out was climbing straight up through the narrow manways.

They heard shouts from down the tunnel. "That's Cobb, he went up to the sun-drift," said Bronson. A few seconds later, a group appeared with Cobb running in the lead. Sullau said, "All of you, climb up to the 22, then head north to the Badger. Go left at the C switch. In about a thousand feet, you'll be blocked by a bulkhead. Break it down and keep going. Cobb, stay here at the switch and stop anybody headed back to the Granite Mountain, then get out. Bronson and I are going down to the 26, we'll be back."

One man broke in, his dirty angular face looking out from under a crumpled cap. "I worked Badger for two years, I can find it."

Sullau told the others, "Follow him," then he and Bronson ran four hundred feet north to the C switch, and turned right. "Jack, I'll take the 17 raise down to the 26. You take the 45," said Sullau. "Anyone you see, tell them climb to the 2200, and out to the Badger."

Bronson started toward the 45 raise. "Meet you on the 26," he yelled.

Sullau stood at the opening to the 17 manway, turned off the compressed air at the joint and hammered a rail spike on a pipe. It rang into the stope and he yelled down, "Fire!" then jumped on the ladder, yelling at each floor as he descended, "Anyone here?"

On the seventh floor down a man answered, "Hey yeah! What's on?"

"How many of you?" Sullau called.

"Five."

Sullau ran back across the planks in the dark. The men peered out from where their candles were lit, lunch buckets in their laps. Shovels and wheelbarrows and tools were strewn around them.

"Fire in the shaft. It's bad. Climb up to the 22. Go north and cross over into the Badger."

By the time Sullau reached the sill he was breathing hard. Bronson was yelling on the manway farther down the drift, then he came clattering out and met Sullau.

"Found nine men. Sent them to the 22."

"I found five. You check the stopes further out. I'm going back inside the Edith May."

Bronson yelled, "Damn, be careful!" But Sullau was already out of sight.

***

The fire roared up the shaft to the 2200 level and at the same time, spread downward following the tangled cable, jumping across sections of the torn insulation, growing larger until the side timbers burst into flames from the heat. When it reached the 26, there was no smoke at the station, just a growing breeze as the fire sucked huge amounts of air into the shaft, feeding the giant blowtorch above.

***

In a stope above the 2800 sill, George Felutovich and his partner had been working a shoot of ore, running a buzzie. When the water went off, they decided to clean out their sputtering drill. Small and wiry, he hardly came to the shoulder of his partner, and spoke Serbian better than English. "She lose pressure, she ain't work right," he said, talking to himself and tinkering with the valves. "Shifter Tregonning, he told me we need to blast, and I will blast."

Parts were laid out across the planks, drill bits leaned against the rock. A fine dust from their earlier drilling filled the air. Felutovich leaned over the parts, selected one carefully, then deftly fit it back into the drill casing. He held his face up close to the metal and squinted in frustration, "Damn."

"Hot in here," said his partner, coiling up the air hose. "Did the water boy come by?"

"Maybe. We check it."

They climbed down the squeaking ladders from the sixth floor to the sill and backtracked on the drift to where the water barrel was. Felutovich worked the stop cock and only a few drips trickled out.

"Pfah! No water." Felutovich slapped the keg with his hand in disgust, "We ain't going to work when we ain't got no drink."

90

Someone hurried down the crosscut toward them, his light bobbing up and down. Felutovich said to his partner, "Maybe he know about the water."

The man stopped, agitated. "There's a fire! Beat it to the station."

Felutovich stared at him, "Fire?"

"Yes! Get out now!"

"What's Tregonning say?" asked Felutovich.

"He's down below. Get moving! Climb the manways."

"Okay, okay!" Felutovich rushed to the raise he knew went to the 2600. Reaching the opening, he looked down the tunnel and saw lights, a group of men bunched up at the next raise. "Them men, they can't get up there," said Felutovich to his partner. "They don't know where they're going."

The drifts and raises in the area were complex and only the experienced miners had figured out the maze of workings. The vein split in different directions, and drilling had left a floret of dead-ends with raises that climbed part way to the next level. Only one of the manways went straight to the 26.

"Hey!" Felutovich yelled, "You're going the wrong way! This is the raise. Go here!" He stood waving his lamp and directed the men into the raise. "Hurry!"

The group climbed and came out on the 26, a hundred feet from the Speculator station. The air was clear and they crowded through the Edith May tunnels toward the Granite Mountain with Felutovich leading and encouraging them, "The station tender, he hoist us!"

A faint crackling noise sounded ahead of them as they ran through the final crosscut toward the station. In the tunnel, instead of the familiar pale light of the station, there was a reddish flickering glow. Felutovich was in the lead and took the last turn. A blast of heat stopped him, then drove him back, and the men collided with each other as the leaders retreated.

"Oh my Christ!"

The group looked in disbelief. The 26 station roared in flames and a strong draft pulled hard into the shaft. Men shouted in horror and panic, swearing, throwing down their hats and buckets. Several dropped to their knees, crying and praying.

"Back to the Spec!" Felutovich yelled.

They ran for the Speculator station, turning two bends in the direction of the shaft and down a long straightaway. Some of the men stumbled in the narrow track beside the wall, others stutter-stepped between the rail ties. "She's after the next turn!" But suddenly the crosscut before them was filled with smoke.

"We're trapped!" someone shouted.

Felutovich yelled, "Is both shafts on fire?" ·

The group panicked and broke apart, some running wildly back toward the burning Granite Mountain station. "No! Stay here! Climb up!" yelled Felutovich and grabbed several of the men to stop them. He turned to go back and ran straight into Sullau, who appeared out of the smoke from the Speculator, his sleeve over his face.

Relieved to see the foreman Felutovich yelled, "Boss!"

Sullau grasped Felutovich's shoulder, "Let's go boys, we're getting off the 2600." He gestured for the other men to follow, "Stay together! Head north to the 45 manway, come on!"

They broke through the smoke around the Spec shaft, and after several minutes of hard running, Sullau stopped them at a raise. He split the group of twenty, "Half climb here, half go to the next raise so we don't break the ladders. Hundred feet that way - Number 51. Bronson is at the top on the 2400."

Ten men went up one narrow chute, rung after rung, ladder after ladder for twenty-eight floors, while the other group climbed the second manway. Felutovich misjudged the opening to a landing and got kicked in the face by the man above. Men at the bottom stacked up on the rungs, waiting for those above and yelling, "Go!"

Sullau's voice boomed down from above, "Don't overload the ladders!"

One by one the men popped from the ladderway onto the 2400 sill. Sullau felt relieved getting off the 26, but there was still a long way to go. *We have to get up higher, farther north toward the Badger or well be trapped.*

The smoke swirled out of the manway they had just left. *Damn, it's already here.* It had followed them up, and Sullau knew any minute it would be rolling at them from the 24 station. He made a quick decision, "Keep climbing, we have to get to the 2200."

The manway through the next level went through a mined out stope. Sections were caved in and the men clambered upward over rocks and splintering timbers.

Felutovich swung up the ladder, reaching the 2200 first. He felt loose rock on the final landing and crawled over it. He felt around in the dark, as another man crowded up the ladder behind him. Shoulder to shoulder they fumbled at the wall, but there was no opening. The manway had been closed off by nailed planks.

"She's boarded up!" Felutovich yelled down.

Sullau yelled back, "Break the middle out."

Felutovich hit his shoulder against the middle of the planks, but bounced off.

"Too thick!"

Men balanced on the ladder below him, holding onto the rungs, covering their mouths with their shirts as the smoke rose up from below.

Felutovich kicked loose a smaller plank and pried it into a small opening near the floor, loosening the thick spike nails. Another man grabbed the end and they both threw their weight against it. With a screech, the nails on one end pulled out. They kicked out the plank and then pried against the one above, working it loose until Felutovich could squeeze through. Standing on the other side, he wrenched the center plank free. Sullau and the rest of the men crawled into the drift.

They had climbed six hundred feet up and had run all the way eastward in the mine. Exhausted, Sullau dropped to the ground, taking deep breaths, wavering in and out of consciousness.

Felutovich looked at him anxiously. "Boss, I get some water for you," and ran down the drift holding his lantern. He reached a four-way rail switch, tracks going down both tunnels, and looked down the main crosscut. In the dim light, boils of smoke slowly rolled toward him. *She come from the 22 Station*, he thought. He found a two-gallon water barrel tucked into the side timbers, opened the top and dipped out a heaving drink, then hauled the barrel back for the others.

Sullau was still lying flat on his back, his hand over his face.

That Sullau, he's done in, thought Felutovich. "You okay, Boss?"

Sullau waved the question off, eyes closed, and asked, "What's it like down that way?"

"She's smoky, but we can walk," said Felutovich. "The far side, I don't think we can."

"How far did you go?"

"To switch station, three hundred feet. The main drift after, she's bad. And more smoke coming."

Sullau said nothing, but thought, *The smoke is blocking the way to the Badger.*

The men waited, afraid, not knowing where to go. Sullau lay there and nobody bothered him. He had been in smoke continuously, and he was more tired than he had ever felt. He fought to remember, *Where was that other connection?* The old one he had worked in years ago that led into the Badger. They had partly filled it and bulkheaded the end to control the air flow. He fumbled through the haze of his mind. *It was to the left.* They had drilled another tunnel three hundred feet to the Snowball and the new drift had become the connection. *That's where it is*, he recalled. *The other side of the rail switch, on the left.*

But the men, he thought, *they won't know where to look*.

Sullau gathered his strength, then rose to his feet without a word. He raised his lamp and said, "Come on boys."

They passed a working drift with stacks of tools jettisoned by the miners. Sullau pointed, "Take some of these – the hammers, saw, and that axe. There'll be another bulkhead to get through."

Felutovich grabbed a saw and his partner a twelve-pound sledge, another picked up the axe.

They got to the switch. Sullau hesitated and asked the group, "Anybody game to go through that smoke? There's a raise on the left side in the next two hundred feet. That's our opening to the 2000."

Felutovich piped up, "I go, but will anybody follow me?"

94

Another miner said, "Yeah, I be on your back."

Felutovich struck off down the drift. His mouth was parched and his lantern flickered low. The farther he went, the clearer the air got, but there was a sickly sweet smell that quickly became almost overwhelming.

She's gas, he thought.

He hurried on, eyes squinting and stinging, lungs starving for air. A feeling of franticness welled up.

Where's the raise? He could not find it, feeling along the rough wall, holding the lantern close. Frustrated, he walked further and shook his head, "It's not here."

They started back, but Sullau met them halfway, walking slowly along the drift with a labored gait. He stopped and leaned on the wall. "Did you find it?" he asked.

"I ain't seen no hole anywhere."

"Come with me."

Behind Sullau were the rest of the men, walking silently in the smoke. Sullau peered up and down at the wall on the left side of the drift, counting the timber sets. "Should be near 21..."

After another twenty yards, he pointed to a broken hole with loose rock packed into it.

"Here."

"What you mean? This is caved."

"This is it," Sullau insisted. "The old raise to the 2000."

Felutovich looked questioningly. Sullau insisted, "This is the old way to the Badger. It's been back-filled with waste rock."

Felutovich quickly pulled out rubble to widen the opening, and several men formed a relay behind him.

"Smoke's coming bad," a man called.

Felutovich pulled at the rock and they cleared a space for the men to pass. The old passageway angled upward steeply, heaps of shattered rock nearly filled it where the top of the tunnel had caved in, and in places cracked slabs hung precariously from the ceiling. Water dripped from the top, leaving the men to crawl through the muck. They entered one by one, until a man started to cry with a frantic voice in the dark. "I can't go in there."

Felutovich led, calling over his shoulder, "I not care where I go. I not stay in smoke." He climbed into the cave, pushing his lantern ahead of him. "Follow me."

The men piled in one after the other, following Felutovitch, on hands and knees, groveling in the muddy darkness up the broken ground.

"Don't touch the top!" yelled Sullau, "She's loose!" The men lowered themselves, elbows torn by the sharp rock edges. Felutovitch's lamp shown weakly, jerking and fluttering as he crawled.

After several hundred feet, he half-stood and clambered over the piles of rock, bending low to keep his head from hitting the ceiling. In a few more minutes, they came up against a wall, and Felutovich showed his light on it. The planks were streaked with crusted minerals.

Sullau caught up to Felutovich. "It goes into the Badger," he said. "Break it down." Then he slouched against a timber, exhausted and watching.

Felutovich held up his lantern. His partner swung the sledge hammer. With a dull *thwack* it left a divot in one of the thick planks. He swung again, another deep dent. Felutovich urged him on, "Harder! Hit again!"

Another swing and the center plank broke out. Felutovich wrenched it loose, and a sudden draft blew through the hole from their tunnel into the Badger drift. Smoke poured past them and snuffed out his lantern.

A man yelled behind them in a terrified voice, "Has anybody light?"

"Come on, I give you light!" Felutovich yelled. He put the self-lighter up to the wall and rasped it across the rock. A stream of sparks came, a little flame hissed and lit the carbide gas. He cupped his hands around to protect it, and weak light splayed into the black drift, the flame fluttering in the draft. He caught glimpses of men's scared faces, eyes and sweaty cheeks glistening.

Sullau's voice cut through, weak but clear, "We're close."

"Two more swings," said the man with the sledge, and reared up and swung, snapping another plank. The hammer hit again, leaving a hole just big enough for a man.

Sullau waved the men on, "Get to the Badger station."

Felutovich squeezed through, then one by one the rest crammed through the hole and he led the group with the weak glow of his lamp. Straggling along, they reached a switch and followed the rails into a larger crosscut with a trolley wire above. Electric lights showed ahead and the men sobbed as they ran. They struck the station and fell on their knees. Felutovich rang the signal bells, and tried to count the men. *Thirteen. But we were twenty in the Spec...*

Rescuers came down in a cage, two of them wearing helmets.

"Where'd you come from?" they asked.

"From the Spec. Fire, smoke. Sullau help us."

"You mean the foreman?"

"Yes."

"Where is he?" the Badger man asked.

Felutovich looked around. "I don't know. He was at bulkhead with us!"

"Which drift did you come out of?"

Felutovich waved his arms in frustration, "I don't know this Badger. We break through. Sullau saved us. You find him!"

The Badger men conferred, "Drift 2042 along the North State vein. That's the connection into the Spec," and the two helmet men set off into the drifts.

The cage tender shepherded Felutovich and the others into the cages and rang the Badger's hoist engineer. In a few minutes, they were lifted to the surface and stepped out, blinking at the lights shining from the Badger's headframe.

CHAPTER ELEVEN

CHAOS ON THE 700

John Camits and John Boyce shoveled by candlelight at the bottom of stope 35, filling ore cars on the 700 level. A quarter after midnight, over the sharp clatter of the ore hitting the gut of the car, they heard running and shouts.

Camits stopped mucking, looked toward the drift and asked, "What's going on?"

The footsteps thudded past and a man yelled out, "Fire!"

"What the hell?"

Another called, "Get out!" and they heard footsteps head down the drift toward the Spec station.

They looked at each other, "Who was that?"

"Wasn't shifter Weigenstein."

Stepping into the drift the air was clear, but there was a smell. Boyce held up his lantern and peered at the timbers. A haze filled the top of the tunnel.

Harsh shouts and scurrying forms rushed toward them, "Goddamn it, run!"

"Where do we go?" cried Camits.

They started running toward the Speculator shaft with the other men.

"The 651 manway! Climb to the 600 Spec station," yelled Boyce.

They crammed into the manway and started up the tight ladders. As they reached the third floor, rocks rattled down on the thick boards above them. Standing on a rung, Camits quickly braced his other foot against the opposite wall, leaned and then covered his head with his arms. The debris bounced down the ladderway and off his arms and shoulders. Boyce was right below him, sheltered by Camits' body.

"She's coming down!"

The section of ladder above them was broken and the rock lay in heaps on the landing where the timbermen had been trying to rebuild the manway.

"It's caved, can't get up!"

Smoke and dust came down the chute in a choking smog. Camits stuck his head up the opening into the floor, staring at the broken ladder overhead. "Shit!" he cursed.

Above came the sounds of more falling rock and men clambering down toward them, screaming, "Get down to the 700!"

"No!" Boyce screamed back. "Go back up!"

A frantic shouting match in the dark and the men above yelled, "Weigenstein said get to the Granite!" More scuffling and suddenly a dozen feet were on the broken ladder above them, knocking rocks loose. "We're coming down!"

Camits yelled up, "The raise is caved!"

Boyce screamed, "Bad smoke down here!"

But the men kept coming, jumping and falling down the broken cross pieces, kicking rocks down on everything below. The two groups clashed at the landing. Boyce and Camits were outnumbered in the tangle and turned back, their fingers stomped and heads kicked by the desperate group above them.

Reaching the 700 sill in the smoke, they stepped to the side as the men from the 600 shoved their way out and ran toward the Granite Mountain. Boyce grabbed Camits' shoulder, pulling him the other direction. "Come on, back toward the stope. Let's go to the manway on the Old Spec side and we'll climb up there."

They ran back to their stope, but others came at them down the drift. As they got to the opening, Boyce held his lantern up, looking in disbelief at the black wall rolling toward them.

They heard shouts, and men stampeded from both directions, blinded. The smoke filled the passage and all the lamps went out, men ran and tripped over the top of each other.

Cries of despair rang down the tunnel.

"My God, my God!"

"My wife! My babies!"

Feeling for the opening in the wall, Camits and Boyce ducked into the cul-de-sac where they had been working. The air inside was breathable but dense smoke eddied around the entrance, filtering inward. Camits scurried toward the back wall, anywhere to get away. Boyce tripped and landed on his stomach, quickly pushed up on his hands and felt the rounded air hose on the floor between his fingers.

"Smoke's on us John!" Camits cried desperately, crouched against the back wall. His voice trembled, listening to the screams outside, "We're going to die!"

Boyce pulled out his candleholder and jabbed the sharpened end into the air hose, stabbing, twisting, and prying, until it tore through the thick rubber. He wrenched it back and forth, opening a jagged hole and the high pressure air shot out, blowing his hat off. "Come here!" he yelled to Camits, "I have air!"

Camits joined him, and they peeled off their coats and shirts, pulled them tight over their heads, clutching the hose to their chests and lay down face to face. Air shot from the ragged hole and hissed deafeningly a few inches from their mouths, shooting into their faces and up their noses, shoving under their eyelids. They could not see or hear, but they could breathe.

Out in the drift all life was silenced, and the last cries stopped as the thick smoke rolled through.

Hours ebbed by and they huddled close. The air inflated the coats like balloons and their bare backs were covered by the falling soot. All sense of time disappeared.

Boyce shifted his cramping hand and one edge of his coat flew up. He stifled a breath of the hot fumes and reached blindly for the whipping cloth as their precious air escaped. Camits caught the coat tail and pulled it back tight around them.

After several hours the pressure in the hose began to weaken. They were dazed by the constant blast of air and noise, and only gradually became aware they were losing their link to life. With a surge of fear, Camits slipped out of his coat and smelled the air. "Still bad!" he yelled in Boyce's ear. They brought their faces closer to the hose, seeking the last fresh air as the hiss faded and their garments fell flat against them. The reek of smoke seeped through; with a sinking feeling, Boyce thought, *The air is failing.*

More time passed and they could only take shallow breaths. Boyce again tested the air around them, and the smoke seemed lighter. "It's starting to clear," he said to Camits. They waited another half hour until almost nothing was coming out of the hose. They had no choice.

"Only chance is make it to the Spec shaft," said Boyce. "You ready?"

They peeled their coats off their heads, lit the lamps, and clambered into the drift. Fine ash puffed from each footstep and a sharp smoky tang hung in the air.

Lifting his lantern, Camits stopped. Blackened bodies were strewn down the tunnel in front of them. They hobbled to the first one, a man slumped against the wall with his feet across the rail tracks. Camits rolled him over, brushing off a layer of ash and holding his lantern low to see who it was. "It's Ramsey," he said, and patted the man's cheek gently. The skin was hard and the face vacant.

"Ramsey, wake up." Camits stared into the fixed gaze and its stillness unnerved him.

"He's dead," said Boyce.

Camits crossed the man's stiff arms, then set him upright as if Ramsey were leaning against the rock wall.

Bodies of fellow miners littered the tunnel, motionless. The two men made their way down the drift toward the Speculator shaft, stepping carefully among the silent forms.

Ahead they saw light moving. "Someone's alive," said Boyce.

Three men came out of a side drift, wearing goggles and heavy breathing apparatus. Camits shrank back from the strange forms, "Who are you?"

The startled rescuers stared at the two men, hair tangled, faces glazed, and hurriedly pulled their mouthpieces out, "Where did you come from?"

"Stope 35," Camits motioned behind them.

The helmet men stood there, baffled, "You rescuing?"

"No, we been holed up since the smoke hit."

"Jesus, are there any other men?"

"Lots of men. But they're all dead."

CHAPTER TWELVE

REVERSING THE FANS

Barnicoat's steel-toed boots flew over the ground as he ran the three hundred yards to the Speculator. He shouted to the guard at the gate, "It's Barnicoat, the topman, I have to get to the shaft!" Stacks of timber rose 20 feet over his head, and the silhouette of the compressor house loomed to his side with its dark smokestacks. Lights projected through the small windows into tight squares of muddy ground, and he cut along the shadowed walkways with the blacksmith's shop on his left, the tall hoist engine house on his right, and came out the other side under the headframe. He saw Pat Burns, the Spec topman, talking with O'Keefe the timekeeper. Barnicoat asked, "You know where the head electrician is?" Burns shook his head. "Haven't seen him."

"Joe, what are you doing here?" asked O'Keefe.

"There's a fire in the Granite Mountain. Night foreman Sullau's underground. You've got to call Braly quick, Frink too, and the Anaconda's helmet crew."

"What? Who's in charge over there?"

"Nobody. Sullau and the whole shift are caught below. Get Braly fast as you can."

"I'll call him," and O'Keefe ran toward the office.

Barnicoat turned to Burns and the men who had gathered around, "Where is the electrician?"

"Try the compressor house," shouted one of them.

Barnicoat dashed back through the mineyard buildings to the compressor house. He found the electrician in the basement and quickly explained. The older man listened intently and nodded, "I'll get the power up. Gem's on the same circuit as the Granite Mountain shaft. Blown circuit, or somebody shut it down."

At the office, O'Keefe dialed the manager's home, which was two hundred yards up the hill from the Speculator. The phone rang repeatedly and O'Keefe strained to keep his composure. Finally a woman's voice said, "Hello?"

102

"Mrs. Braly? I'm sorry Ma'am, I know it's late. Could I speak to the boss? Tell him it's O'Keefe. Urgent."

O'Keefe nervously tapped his fingers on the desk.

A familiar baritone sounded on the other end of the telephone, "Yes?"

"Mr. Braly? This is O'Keefe. You got to get here quick. Men just come from the Granite Mountain, saying there's a fire in the shaft. Sullau's down trying to put it out. There's four hundred men under. They don't got no way out."

"Be right there," said Braly in a clipped voice, slammed the receiver down, and ran for his door.

Braly headed to the Speculator, rushing down the dark slope from his house that overlooked the mineyard. Beyond the Speculator, the hill fell away in a desolation of waste rock lit by angled lights coming from mineyards and train tracks crossing the hill, and at the bottom, thousands of lights of Meaderville and east Butte spilling down into the valley. Crossing the trestle over the railroad tracks, to his left he saw the smoke swirling around the Granite Mountain headframe and in front of him, a trace of smoke coming up the Speculator shaft. *Goddamn!* he swore to himself.

Alarmed and breathless, Braly ran into Barnicoat near the Spec shaft, "Joe, what's going on?"

"We got a fire down on the 2400," Barnicoat tried to explain. "The power is out in the Granite Mountain shaft and at the Gem. I came..."

Braly pointed at the thin trail of smoke now coming from the Speculator shaft, "Smoke's coming from *both* shafts!" The scope of the problem became clear, "It must be all through the Edith May!"

"I found the night electrician," said Barnicoat, "He's turning on the ..."

Braly interrupted, "We got to drive smoke away from the men. Where's the Spec topman, Burns? You boys get the Spec fan reversed and seal the collar."

Braly ran into the office with Barnicoat on his heels, and grabbed the telephone to call the night engineers at the Gem and then the Rainbow, the other two ventilation shafts. He spoke curtly, "Reverse your fans, quick as possible, full downcast," then turned to Barnicoat, "We'll push as much air as we can down the Spec, Gem, and Rainbow. Make the Granite Mountain a chimney, and flush the smoke out of the workings."

Barnicoat broke in, "Norman, power's off at the Gem too. We don't know why. I just told the electrician to get it back on, the Gem and the Granite Mountain."

"Jesus," cursed Braly, throwing his hands in the air. "Okay, you take care of the Spec. Reverse the fan here. I'll do the Gem." He disappeared, running full tilt out of the yard and down the hill.

Smoke now engulfed the area under the Speculator headframe, and a group of men stood just outside the pall.

"Where's topman Burns?" Barnicoat shouted.

One of the station tenders answered anxiously, "Paddy? He went down the shaft with a helmet."

Barnicoat was incredulous, "What the hell? Why?"

"Shifter Goodell and him, they was getting Burns' brother-in-law. Down the 600."

"Oh Christ!" Barnicoat threw up his hands, "Here, come with me," he waved impatiently. "Where's the fan mechanic? Find him and meet me at the ventilation fan, tell him we got to fix it."

Barnicoat ran around the edge of the headframe to the tunnel where the huge fan was mounted. Smoke trailed up the tunnel, which slanted underground and connected with the shaft below the ore pockets. Without waiting for the mechanic, he yanked the wrench off the wall and began loosening the locking nuts on the side of the fan. He had gotten one nearly off when the mechanic appeared and he handed the wrench over, "Fast as you can, open her up and change the louvers, Braly wants this reversed. I'm gonna brattice up the shaft. We got to drive air down with everything this fan's got."

"Reverse her?"

"Braly's forcing the Granite upcast. Gem, Rainbow, and Spec, all down. Going to drive smoke up the Granite."

The mechanic ground out his cigarette against the tunnel wall. "Got it." He took the wrench and went at the bolts.

Barnicoat hustled back into the yard and pointed to two groups of men, "You and you. We're building a brattice over the shaft. Get the cut boards there," he pointed at the piles in the yard. "The chute planks. Put them two thick. Find some canvas."

Out of the corner of his eye, he saw a geyser of flame erupt down at the Granite Mountain, flickering and pulsing under the headframe. He turned to look.

"What the hell is going on there?" someone asked.

"That a cage?" said the tender, "On fire?"

Barnicoat felt a sudden stab, *Where are Conroy and Sheridan?*

A man came panting into the yard, running to Barnicoat, "You in charge here?"

"Hell if I know," said Barnicoat testily.

The man looked confused, and impatiently Barnicoat demanded, "What is it?"

"I'm from the Diamond, Foreman O'Neill, he say to tell you's guys, there been nine Spec men come through our mine. They's from the 2200 into our workings."

"Nine of our men?"

"Yea, that's so. Nine. O'Neill, he say we're hoisting our shifts right now. Men's going out the Gray Rock and Corra. He's bratticing the 1800 connection to your workings, for to keep the smoke out of the Diamond."

Barnicoat felt his heart grabbing as the seriousness dawned on him, *What in God's name is going on down there?* He gave the man's shoulder a quick slap, "Tell O'Neill thanks for the head's up."

He turned to the station tender. "Did you hear what he said?" and jerked his thumb at the messenger from the Diamond, "They got our men coming through the Diamond and Gray Rock. Anyone come up here? What numbers you got?"

"Hoisted maybe thirty of ours just before you came, shifter Goodell's men, and him too, from the 22."

"Well, where's he now?"

"Down with Burns, they got helmets and went down. To the 600, I think."

"Anybody from the 600 come up?"

"Nobody."

Barnicoat closed his eyes, "Holy God, 600 to 800 levels must be in smoke! What about Weigenstein's men? Fifty of them. I let them down at shift change. How many you seen?"

"None. But they doesn't hoist here. You's hoist them through the Granite." He looked over at the pall of smoke rising out of the Granite Mountain, "Ain't nobody coming up that shaft now."

They heard the harsh bleating of the Spec shaft's squawker and turned to the shaft collar. Someone yelled, "Men hoisted!"

Barnicoat quickly stopped the group working on the brattice, "Wait on that timber!"

A cage came up. The doors slammed open as it was still moving, and Burns and Goodell burst out in a run, pulling a third man by the shoulders of his coat, dragging him into the yard. His legs were limp and his head flopped.

They stopped outside the shroud of smoke and Burns knelt, pushing on the man's chest. Goodell threw down his helmet, yelling to the men standing nearby, "Get some oxygen!" They stared and didn't move.

"What the hell's wrong with you?" he screamed, "Get a bottle of oxygen!"

Goodell kneeled next to Burns, frantically pumping on the man's chest. Barnicoat ran to them and Goodell glanced up.

"Burns' brother-in-law. Station tender on the 600."

"The 600 – it's that bad?" Barnicoat asked.

"It's impossible," said Goodell, "Can't live half a minute without a helmet."

"What about Weigenstein? The shifts on the 600 and 700?"

Goodell's jaw tightened, "Don't know. Was all we could do to get twenty feet from the station with helmets and drag Pete back."

Someone handed them an oxygen bottle, and Burns cupped the rubber mask over the downed man's mouth, still pushing on the man's chest, quietly pleading to the lifeless body, "Come on my Pete, come on…"

The Spec's first aid officer joined Burns, and Goodell pulled Barnicoat away, talking in a rush, "We couldn't see nothing, he was down flat, other bodies too, couldn't count them."

Burns knelt there in the middle of the mineyard, staring at his brother-in-law, his gray pallor unchanging.

The signal bells rang again. "Men hoisting!" came the call across the yard.

"The 600. Weigenstein!"

A set of stacked cages came up and men quickly popped out of one cage after another, running from below the headframe with shirts held over their mouths, tripping and staggering into the yard.

The last man out of the bottom cage was Weigenstein, shift boss for the 600 and 700 levels, his face ashen and grim.

"Aren't there more?" asked Barnicoat.

Weigenstein looked at him, eyes swollen, "This is it."

"What you mean? Should we send a cage back down?"

"No, the others are dead."

"My God, how many?"

Weigenstein answered slowly, "Twenty at least. I sent them down to the 700. Thought it was safe. Told them head to the Granite to get hoisted."

"Jesus," the two men looked at each other.

"I killed them," said Weigenstein blankly. "My own men."

Barnicoat tilted his head back, it was more than he could bear, "Take five. Just rest, Albert."

Weigenstein waved him off. "I got to do something to help. Edith May stopes are hell."

The mechanic appeared, "We got her reversed Joe."

"Turn it on!" said Barnicoat.

"Ain't going to blow down much if you don't cover the shaft."

"Just get it going!" The electrician disappeared into the inclined ventilation shaft, and a low drone grew as the fan's ten-foot blades whirred up to speed. The breeze at the shaft grew quickly into a strong gust, driving the smoke away and down the shaft.

Barnicoat set to finishing the brattice, and he heard the Granite Mountain's steam whistle blast out ten shrieks, the signal for a major accident. The other mines picked it up, until the entire hill reverberated with the whistles.

Down in the city the urgency drove through the streets, and every miner off-shift in the saloons stepped outside and thought, *Dear Lord, keep my friends safe.* And every wife in bed alone rose to listen and begin her own pleading, *Dear God, let my husband live.*

It was one in the morning, Saturday, June 9th.

CHAPTER THIRTEEN

DEEP IN THE SPECULATOR

At midnight, the telephone rang at Con O'Neill's house a quarter mile west of the Granite Mountain shaft. He was the foreman of the Diamond mine, a robust Irishman and a favorite of the men.

Throwing off the covers he crossed the room and answered the call, lips pursed, listening to the frantic voice on the other end of the line.

His wife woke, "What's going on?"

"That was the time-keeper at the Granite Mountain. He says there's a fire at their mine."

"Don't go, Con," she said, "Someone else will take care of it."

"Yes, but I got to make sure it doesn't hurt ours. I'll sort things out and be back."

He swung his coat over his back and hurried out of the house, closing the front door carefully so he didn't wake their small daughters. Trotting toward the Diamond, he left the far end of Center Street and crossed over the edge of the ridge to the east side of the hill. Cresting the top, he could see smoke rising from the Granite Mountain.

"*Aie*, that's bad," he said to himself and started to run.

At the shaft collar, the station tender Toomey was relieved to see him.

"Boss, there's a fire in the Granite Mountain."

A little whistle of air came through O'Neill's teeth as he thought, "Yeah, I got a call. You know anything?" he asked in his tight brogue.

"Nope."

"Let's find out what's happening down there." O'Neill turned to the Diamond topman, "Where is the chippy cage?"

"It's on the 1600, station tender Dennihey's unloading timber."

"Ring the tender up. I want to talk with him."

109

"Okay, it'll take a couple minutes."

O'Neill stepped over to the edge of the Diamond yard and looked at the Granite Mountain. *What the hell?* he thought. *That shaft should be downcast, pushing air to the men below.* The realization struck him. *My God, they won't have any air.*

He walked quickly back to the shaft collar and found Toomey. "Gas is going to come into our workings, through the Spec-Badger drift on the 1800. Where's Lowrey?" he said over the noise of the yard. "We got to move as fast as we can."

The short Englishman poked his head up from behind an ore car. "You want me?"

"I need your help. Both of you. We're building a brattice on the 1800."

The chippy cage came to the surface and Dennihey stepped out, his face questioning, "I got a signal to come up?"

"Is the air clear below?" asked O'Neill.

"I was on the 1600, it's good as she ever is."

"What about the 1800?"

"Don't know."

"Okay, wait a minute, we're taking a load down."

O'Neill, Toomey, and Lowrey collected tools and supplies from the carpenter's shop and returned to the shaft collar. When they got back, a group of men stood gesturing and arguing.

"What's going on?" O'Neill demanded.

"Gray Rock called," said a clerk from the office. "They just hoisted nine men from the Spec. Said they came from the Edith May."

"Send a runner down to the Spec office," O'Neill ordered, "Tell them their men are escaping through our mine." He turned to the topman, "Tell all the shift bosses to raise their men as fast as they can. Ring the skips up and put the stacked cages on."

"The Spec boys must have come across on the 1800 crosscut or on the 22 connection to the High Ore. If they left the doors open, the gas will come right into our shaft." They loaded all the materials onto the chippy cage.

Blasts of a steam whistle sounded from the Speculator and more from the Granite Mountain. Then all across the hill, whistles from all the mines started blowing the signal for a major accident.

Grim faced, O'Neill turned to Dennihey and said, "Take us to the 1800."

The tender rang the hoist engineer to lower them, *five bells – pause – three bells*. The men held on the overhead steel bar and their cage dropped into the shaft.

O'Neill was relieved when they got to the 1800 and the air was clear. "We need to go down the 1804 a little ways." They unloaded all the boards and materials from the cage and hurried to the tunnel, fifty feet from the shaft. Five timber sets farther, O'Neill stopped, "Let's build it here, hustle now." They dumped their loads. "We'll put up a board frame with lagging across it, and then nail the canvas on. That should be enough."

Toomey and Lowrey went to work, nailing lagging boards upright between the timbers as O'Neill unfolded the sheet and began stretching it carefully across to block the air flow.

"Won't be airtight," said Toomey.

"Our shaft is downcast, we'll have positive pressure on our side, smoke won't get through the brattice," said O'Neill, "Let's be quick."

The folded sheet stuck together and O'Neill pulled to straighten it. He felt a puff of warmer air and stopped. "Did the draft just change?" he asked the others. Suddenly, there was a gust of hotter air, and he held his hand up to feel the direction. "What the hell?"

"Look!" yelled Lowrey, pointing down the drift.

They turned their lanterns and, in the dim light, saw a wall of black smoke bearing down on them from the Speculator. O'Neill shouted, "Run!" and they turned and fled toward the shaft.

The black cloud drove over them. They could not see the ground and slowed down. After twenty steps Lowrey collapsed.

"Help me with him," yelled O'Neill, and he and Toomey reached down through the murky air feeling for Lowrey's arms, picked him up, one on either side, and dragged him. It was only fifty feet to the station, but Lowrey was limp, legs dangling and his

111

head flopping over. They stumbled over the rails. "Hurry!" yelled O'Neill, "We're almost to the station."

The gas pressed in around them. The two men staggered, then fell to the ground. Toomey got on hands and knees, crawling toward the shaft. O'Neill raised himself, but faltered as the hot black smoke raked his throat. He felt his hands on the gritty floor in front of him, his fingers dug into the crushed gravel, then he vomited.

The station was close. He pictured the drift but his mind spun, confusing distance and directions and he could not orient himself. Crawling forward, his head hit hard against the rock wall. *Angle left*, he ordered himself.

"Toomey!" cried O'Neill. The sound of scuffling came from in front of him, but there was no answer. He crawled forward in slow motion. Everything spun around. His hearing and sight retracted until nothing outside existed but the press of the smoke and his coughing lungs starved for air. He crumpled to the ground fifty feet from the station.

Toomey dragged himself along the rails. He hit the metal sheets and knew he was close. A few feet from the shaft he broke out of the blackness into a gloomy swirl. The breeze from the shaft kept the smoke at bay, and his choking lungs sucked raggedly at the cleaner air. His eyes bulged and stung, but he could see the halo of the burning lantern they had left. He pulled himself closer to the shaft, gasping. Somewhere behind him in the drift there was a rumbling sound, like deep snoring. Like a man dying.

A chippy cage moved down the shaft. The noise reverberated closer and louder. He gazed stupidly at the cables moving in opposite directions in the two ore shafts, something he had seen thousands of times, but now seemed incomprehensible. The cage settled at the level and three helmet men stepped out, looking like tubed monsters in their goggles and big rubber mouthpieces.

They bent over him but Toomey waved them off and pointed back into the smoke, croaking, "Get O'Neill and Lowrey!"

James Calvert, the first helmet man barked, "Crowley, come on!"

The rescuers disappeared. Moments later, they came back dragging O'Neill and left him at the station, then went back and returned hauling Lowrey.

Two of the rescuers wiped O'Neill's face with a towel and slapped his cheeks. "Come on, Con!" pleaded Toomey, rising to his knees, "You're stronger than all of us."

The other rescuer worked on Lowrey. Behind them, Toomey collapsed to the ground.

"There's too much gas!" shouted Calvert, "We have to go up!"

Holding them under the arms, they dragged the unconscious men onto the cage, and rang the hoist. The cage flew upwards, and at the surface, O'Neill, Toomey, and Lowrey were pulled into the yard by helping hands. Three or four men worked on each one, and Toomey revived, opening his eyes. After fifteen minutes he could whisper a few words. The doctor placed oxygen masks on Lowrey and O'Neill, and their chests were compressed and expanded. The activity became more intense but still they sank away, too deeply poisoned, breathing more shallowly until they were gone.

***

Deep in the Speculator on the 2800, Ben Tregonning and Claude Powers stood by the shaft in a pool of electric light, feeling the cool breeze descending from the night far above. Here on the 2800, the rock temperature was more than one hundred degrees. Heat came from every direction and the only respite was the moving air. The deeper into the earth, the hotter the rock. Miners joked it was because you were closer to hell.

A motorman came out of the crosscut pulling a trainload of rock and they watched him dump the ore into the pockets for the skips. Tregonning yelled to him through the clatter, "Everything okay?"

"She's good."

"Next trip, pull the 2807 chute. It's muckbound."

113

"Will do," and he rattled down the crosscut for another load.

Tregonning peeled off his sweat-soaked shirt and wrung it into the crushed rock floor, then flapped it open and pulled it over his head. Bits of grit and rock grated against his back.

A fan droned beside him, pushing air down the shaft for the men below. Another whined a few yards away at the beginning of the crosscut, pulling air from the station and filling a canvas pipe like a balloon, then pushing it into the workings of the 2800. Eventually the air circulated south to the Speculator shaft and then up to the surface.

"Your fans been working?" Tregonning asked Powers.

"Humming like a song since I got here," said Powers.

"My mid-floor men blasted an hour ago and the dust is still hanging there."

"Check the piping down the drift. Could be a joint loose."

"Did that already. Everything's fine," Tregonning said. "I think we got to open up our drill lines. Sullau doesn't want to waste the pressure, but we don't have a choice today."

Another train of ore came in. Tregonning waved at the motorman entering the station and helped him dump the cars.

"Yours is the second load already. You boys been working hard."

"Thanks Boss," said the motorman. "The guys in the stopes are getting the job done."

Tregonning laughed, "Keep it coming."

Covered with a new layer of dust, Tregonning stepped back to Powers' side. Before the two men, the shaft was timbered into four vertical compartments. The big ore skips ran in the two on the left, controlled by the engineer on the surface.

Powers ran a small hoist for a utility cage in the compartment on the right, which served the bottom-most levels of the mine. The hoist's mount was bolted into the rock floor so the engine could lift five tons, and drove a three-foot diameter drum with twelve hundred feet of steel cable wrapped around it, reaching all the way to the sump. It sat hissing slightly, ready to leap into action.

114

The company had blocked the chippy compartment just above him to protect men at the bottom from falling timbers or rock. Powers worked his shift fetching tools or men, and his hands constantly worked the cage up and down from the 2800 to the 3700, nine hundred feet below where men were sinking the shaft further.

As long as the pipes held air pressure, Powers could lift and lower to deliver a steady stream of tools and supplies for the workers below. The bottom of the mine was Powers' world, and the men down there were keenly aware the hoist was the only way to get up and down.

"Ben, you know that cable they was lowering?"

"Yeah?"

"Well, the whole thing fell about two hours ago. It's filling the chippy shaft above us."

"They getting it out?"

"Guess so. You should have heard it, sounded like the whole shaft was caving in," he pointed up. "Lots of water too. Broke the pipes. Scared the hell out of me."

"What's Collins doing now?"

"He came up. Said, 'Ain't no water for the drills.' Pulled his shift, but left two men timbering on the 32."

"They go up top?"

"Yeah. Just those two still below."

"Well, keep track of them," Tregonning said to Powers, "See you in a couple hours." Then he headed down the crosscut to his beat in the Edith May.

Powers turned back to the hoist. Holding a long-beaked can, he oiled the linkages on the engine, thumbing a few drops onto the bearings and working parts. From the shaft came faint rattling echoes, the sounds of loaded ore skips far above, more shaking than noise. Small broken pieces of rock ricocheted down, peppering the timbers and the screen near the shaft opening.

Yells sounded from above, travelling through the shaft. Powers kept oiling the hoist and paid them no mind. Men were always hollering about something. The shouts came again, their tone more shrill and clipped, and he stopped for a moment.

The string of electric bulbs flickered above him. He cast a glance at them. *What's going on?*

They flickered again and went out, leaving Powers in utter darkness. The hum of the ventilation fans spun down into silence.

"Damn," Powers mumbled and reached into his pocket for a candle and matches. He lit the candle and slid it into the well-used holder stuck in the timber next to him, lighting the station dimly.

An urgent shout from above caught his ear. Alarmed, he stepped over to the edge of the shaft, craned his head and peered into the blackness above. Far up the main shaft hovered a bit of trembling orange. This light writhed and danced. It took a few moments before he realized what it was.

"Flames," he whispered.

***

Tregonning was midway through the stope between the 26 and 28 when he heard quick boots thumping above. A lamp flashed, and he jumped to the edge of the landing as another miner barreled down the ladder beside him. He recognized him in the swinging lamplight, the man's eyes darting and anxious.

"Ben! There you are! Big fire above."

"What?"

"Blocking the shaft. They're all scrambling. We got to get out!"

In disbelief he asked, "We can't use the shaft?"

"No!"

Possible routes to the surface flashed through Tregonning's mind. "Get everyone you can find. Climb to the 24, I'll get the men below." He shouted as he left, "At the Spec station, follow the crosscuts south!"

He climbed down to the 2800 and found several of his men. "Head for the 2807 and climb to the 24, then south out the High Ore. The goddamn shaft's on fire."

"You coming?" asked one.

"Collins had two men below, I got to find them."

The man shot him a worried look. "Ben, you should climb with us."

Tregonning ignored him and pointed down the crosscut, "Spread the word as you go. Hit separate drifts."

They split and Tregonning ran for the 2800 Granite Mountain station. In a few quick minutes, his feet pounded across the turnsheets, and Powers' tense face greeted him.

Powers pointed up, "Ben, there's a fire above us."

"I know. Lower me," he said between gasps.

"To the 32? For Collins' men?"

Tregonning nodded, "Yeah, I'm getting them."

"Then what?"

"You raise us, and we'll climb to the 24."

Tregonning jumped on the cage as Powers yelled, "I'll be waiting!" and released the brake.

The cage plummeted down and he held onto the bar overhead, his heart pounding as rock walls rushed by his elbow. Thoughts churned through his mind. *Electricity is off. Pumps went out with the lights.* He instinctively looked down, as if he could see past the steel floor of the cage to the bottom of the shaft. *Water's going to rise fast down there.*

The cage slowed, compressing him downward as it came to a stop at the station. Shadows fell away from his lamp. He stepped out and rang Powers 2-1-2 for *all clear*.

The rough rock walls of the 3200 station crowded close. There was just enough room to get timbers and fifteen-foot lengths of rail through, and for the men to wrestle the drills and equipment out of the shaft and into the crosscut.

With the fans off, the air felt motionless, thick and hot. There was no sound of drills or men working. A stream trickled down the ditch along the wall, emptying into a catchment area next to the shaft, then into a pipe to the pumps five hundred feet below.

Tregonning knew that all the ground water of the mine was funneled into the bottom. With the pumps not working, the sump must have already filled, water was flooding the short crosscuts and rising steadily up the shaft. They did not have much time.

117

Holding his lamp before him, Tregonning trotted down the coarse, muddy tunnel that struck west, until he could see two silhouettes ahead, laboring at the end of the crosscut. The heat was stifling. The men's shirts were off as they pounded wedges to brace the timber set.

"Got to get out!" Tregonning shouted, "There's a fire!"

The men stopped, facing him as he came closer, "What? Where's shifter Collins?"

"He's up top. We got a fire 600 feet above us. We're hoisting to the 28, and climbing out the Spec from there."

Hurrying, they threw their tools down, snatched up clothes, and Tregonning led them back to the station. One of them started to ask, "How bad is ..." but a burning chunk of wood fell past in the ore compartment to their left, striking the edge in a shower of sparks, then plunged toward the rising water at the bottom.

The men looked at Tregonning and a sense of dread descended on them.

He yelled, "Let's go! Now!"

Up on the 28, Powers nervously gripped the steel throttle lever. "Come on Ben, get those guys..."

Out of the corner of his eye, he saw a faint tendril of smoke, swirling like vapor. He stepped over to the main shaft again, holding his candle out. A flaming timber streaked down past him, leaving a trail of smoke in the candlelight. Horrified, he jumped back behind the hoist, using it as a barrier as more debris came rattling down. His impulse was to run, but he held himself back, *You have to wait. Ben needs you. He can't get up without the hoist.*

Crackling and thrumming, a rising crescendo of sounds came from above. He regripped the lever, his palms sweating. He could hear the familiar hiss of the hoist and thought, *We have air. I can lift you Ben.*

A burst of smoke rushed into the station, and Powers pulled his shirt up to cover his face, trying to protect himself from the noxious air, still waiting for the signal bells from below. *Ring me, God damn it.*

***

The men crowded into the cage on the 32, and Tregonning yanked the cord that went up to the bells at the 2800 station. Three fast pulls for *up, now!* They waited long seconds but the cage stayed motionless. He rang again, but there was no reply.

A clattering echo sounded in the ore shaft and a gush of rubble hurtled by, bouncing off the chute planks that protected the chippy shaft from the falling chaos.

He signaled again, three quick rings. "Come on Claude, answer me."

"He must have run for it," said one of the men.

"No, he'd never leave us down here. Something's wrong." A knife edge cut through Tregonning's stomach, *Claude's hurt or knocked out by smoke...*

"Follow me!" he ordered the men as he scrambled up to the top of the chippy cage, climbing sideways into the narrow pump shaft to the right.

"I ain't doing that," one man said, backing away.

"There's nothing coming down the chippy shaft, it's blocked at the 28. The electric wires are out. We can make it up."

The men looked at him anxiously. He called down, his voice sharp and tight, "Climb! There's no other way."

Just above the cage, Tregonning balanced with his feet on the timbers, grasping the pipes and wedging his boot on a bracket. He pulled himself up to the next timber set, while below him, the other men edged into the space, an area a couple of feet wide and five feet front to back. It was narrow enough they could step across and climb from set to set, using the pipes and cables for hand holds. Below was 500 feet of air.

Cautiously, they shuffled on the timbers. Anxious fingers found the pipes, cables, and wall plates, the wedges between the timbers and the rock wall. Anything to hold onto.

Tregonning pushed upward, placing his lantern on the foot-wide timber above him. He moved his hands across until he could grasp the electric cable or the pipe and pull himself up. If he fell, he would take the men below him to the sump.

They figured out the sequences of moves from set to set and climbed upward in a chain, exposed and tenuous. As long as they could focus on the movements, they could stem the fear that washed through them. Tregonning knew he could not falter or none of them would make it. Again and again, he urged the men up the shaft, calling down to them, "We can do it!"

The lanterns lit the shaft around them, darkness ruled everywhere else. They could not see the distance down but they felt it. Sweaty hands grasped, palms slipped, and panic spiked through their bodies.

They finally made it to the 3000 station. Tregonning hauled himself over the edge and onto the turnsheets. Lying down, he gave his hand to the first man and helped him up and over, then the second man.

He seized the signal cord, "Come on Claude," and rang the station at the 28. Nothing.

He let go of the cord and turned to the men, "One more level."

They scrambled back into the pump compartment and made their way upwards as rumbling noises came from above.

Another hundred feet higher, Tregonning put the lantern

on the timber above him. As he pulled himself upward, his hand slipped and hit the lamp. It toppled and slowly rolled off the edge. In disbelief, they watched it plunge past, striking the side of the shaft in a flash of flame and ricocheting down in the dark. One of the men passed his lantern upward, and they continued.

As they approached the 2800 station, the man below Tregonning reached up the pipe for a handhold and started pulling. He was broad-shouldered and heavy, exhausted from the long awkward climb. His hand slipped and he lost his grip. It popped off the pipe and his body swung away from the wall, his face looking upward at Tregonning filled with terror.

Tregonning lay on the timber, stretched down, grabbed the man's shoulder, heaving him back toward the wall until he got ahold of the pipe again. Sharp breaths cut the air.

Tregonning asked, "You okay?"

Unable to answer, the big man fought for control of his body and breath until he could move again. Tregonning steeled himself and willed his arms and legs upward. "We're almost there," he yelled.

At the 28 station, he pulled himself onto the level. Smoke swirled around them. Cinders and gleaming sparks were piled at the opening of the main shaft, a constant rain of debris spilled from the fire above. Rocks bounced past, broken off the walls of the shaft hundreds of feet above by the heat. Tregonning peered around, his lamp barely burning in the gloom. *Where is Powers?*

Dimly he saw the engineer hunched against the hoist engine, his fingers stiff, clenched around the levers.

"Claude!"

He did not respond. Tregonning grabbed his shoulders and pulled him upright. Powers gazed distantly toward Tregonning. "No ... pressure..." he said in a slow, throaty whisper.

The engine was quiet. The compressed air had gone out and there had been nothing Powers could do, but wait.

"Let's get to the 2807 manway," Tregonning said.

CHAPTER FOURTEEN

DUGGAN CONVINCES

The fire intensified like a blast furnace, shaft timbers exploding and flames rushing upwards. With each surge, waves of black smoke billowed across the connecting drifts. Pressure drafts fought with the smoke, forcing it back, driving it up. Drifts flooded with smoke and became impassable, then suddenly opened and men dashed through, until the smoke washed back even denser. The fumes funneled from the Granite Mountain across to the Speculator shaft, then up to higher levels, pushing back into the workings on every level from both sides, into the stopes and manways, shutting off escape.

In the tunnel to the High Ore, John Wirta faced an iron door, armed with only a hammer. It was their only escape, and it was rusted shut. At the first alarm below on the 2600, he had joined eight miners, tumbling out of their stope. They quickly climbed up the manways, rushed past the Speculator shaft toward the High Ore, and straight into the blocked tunnel. Other men crowded up behind, frantic and confused.

"Foreman told us to get out this way."

"Open the damn thing!"

"Can't!" shouted Wirta to the men behind. He pounded on the door hinges with a hail of high-pitched *pings*, chips of rust flying, until they wrenched it open and ran, only to be blocked by a thick concrete wall further down the tunnel.

The hammer was worthless. "Jesus, what are we going to do?" Three men pried up a rail and the group gathered on either side, swinging it like a battering ram. It ricocheted off the hard concrete without making a dent. Terrified, they looked back into the dark tunnel.

"I'm going to blast this thing open!" Wirta yelled. He and his partner Yjra Johnson ran back into the Speculator, and made it to the powder room on the other side of the shaft. He jacked open the lock with a crowbar, shoving its end through the lock and snapping it down. Inside, he stripped off the top of a box of

Hercules powder and quickly popped up fifteen sticks of dynamite, while Johnson got fuses and blasting caps. Racing back down the crosscut, dense smoke filled the Spec station, blocking their way.

"Run through it!" yelled Wirta. They plunged in, but had to turn around, retreating north from the oncoming smoke but not knowing where to go. Two men came out of the dark at them, Cobb and Fowler, headed for the High Ore. Wirta waved them back, "You can't come this way!"

"Damn," said Cobb. He and his swamper Fowler had run from the north country back toward the Speculator. "Can't you get to the High Ore?"

"No," said Wirta, "It's cut off."

Cobb insisted, "Let's climb to the 22. We can get to the High Ore from there."

Wirta quickly set the dynamite down in a side drift. They found a raise and started climbing. Thirty feet up, all of them were choking.

"Down, back to the sill!"

They backed down and into the drift, starting to panic. The men's faces were tense, Cobb looked at Johnson and Wirta, "Back toward the Granite, if we can get past the crosscut to the shaft, we can make it north out the Badger. That's where Sullau was headed."

"Anywhere, just not here," said Johnson.

Wirta mustered his courage, "Let's go!" The others followed as he half-ran, half-stumbled past the crosscut to the Granite station. On the other side, the air cleared.

Down the tunnel they saw waving lanterns in the distance. Fearful voices, harsh and hurried, running toward them. As the group neared, Wirta called, "Where you from?"

"Lynchburg stopes," said one of the men, Joe James.

Wirta yelled, "What're you coming back here for? Head north!"

"Can't, smoke blocked us," said James and wiped his mouth.

Another group joined them, "Who you with?" called out a mucker named Novac.

"Duggan. Over there," James pointed to a slight man. "We was running wild, nowhere to go, and saw him waving a light, telling everyone to head to the High Ore. Got cut off. Then we tried to head north to the Rainbow, but too late."

Cobb said, "Same here. We been running like fools, back and forth between smokes."

"Trapped," said James.

They stood looking at each other, futility in their faces.

Men yelled suggestions. Novac shouted, "We need a box of dynamite. Blast our way out."

"Can't blast the damn smoke. You won't last more than a few breaths," said Wirta.

Novac cast out another suggestion, "We can head up the manway, the Spec connects to the High Ore on the 22."

Cobb stood at Wirta's side, "We couldn't make it."

More men staggered in from the side drifts for the Croesus and Snowball stopes, appearing out of manways and straggling down the 2401 crosscut to the group. Each looked around. Their faces said everything.

Options were down to nothing.

They crowded together in the wider area where a drift split from the main crosscut, shoulder to shoulder in the growing haze. Fear lay heavy on them. The waterboy started crying.

Duggan stood at the center of the group listening to the arguments. He waited for a break, and started speaking quietly, the men craned to listen to the slender, soft-spoken man.

"Listen to me boys," he said. "You can suit yourselves. You can try to make the Spec if you want, or out to the Badger, but my advice is to bulkhead in. That's what I'm going to do, and I recommend you do the same."

There was silence.

Duggan pointed into the drift next to them. "That's the 2471, a dead end. We have clear air still, and we can block it off and wait out the fire."

"You mean, bury ourselves down here?" came a voice from the edge of the group.

"It's our only chance."

124

Cobb stood in front facing Duggan, Fowler at his shoulder. He nodded, "I'm with you."

A man in back protested, "Let's try again for the Spec."

"We've checked every manway and drift," Duggan answered. "Smoke's closing in. We don't have time."

There was no more arguing. The calm voice convinced them. Duggan went into the drift first and the others hurried after him.

Workers had thrown their tools down when the alarm first came, and the men gathered up scattered hammers, saws, lagging boards and chute planks, and tore down canvas ventilation piping, until they dragged along a brangle of materials cobbled from the workings.

James found a submarine tank of water for the drills, "It's dirty, but she's drinkable." Wirta found a two-gallon keg of drinking water and carried it along the rail tracks. After another turn, three hundred feet into the drift, the air was good. No gas, no smoke.

Duggan set down his load of lagging boards and said, "Build it here."

A compressed air pipe ran the length of the roof, hung in the upper corner from the timber sets, going all the way back into the dead end drift where the drill was. Several of the men eyed the pipe and nodded, brightening their spirits, "We got air with that." They piled their findings, separating the wood, canvas, and tools.

"Let's take a break for five," said one of the men, red-faced and puffing from the run.

"No, we have to make all speed," Duggan insisted. "If the gas gets here first, we're dead."

They began. Cobb and Wirta tore the canvas piping into sections, slitting it with their knives in pieces the width of the tunnel. Others shoveled dirt and sand into dynamite boxes at the working face and brought them to the growing bulkhead.

Four men worked at a time, there was no room for more. Duggan and a man named Stewart quickly nailed planks into the timbering on both sides, securing the bottom, they used the lagging and planks to make a frame a foot thick, then poured in sand and dirt. Men pulled off their filthy pants, sweaters, shirts, socks, nailing them onto the surface to cover the cracks and packed them in with more dirt.

"Save some canvas to make a second brattice."

"Leave a hole on the side," motioned Duggan, "we'll stuff it with a shirt so we can test the air outside."

Stewart stopped for a second, head cocked upward. The first wisps of smoke pooled up to the bulkhead.

"Time's up."

Cobb stood holding the last boards as Duggan nailed.

"Wait," Cobb said, standing outside the bulkhead. He took a rail spike and hurriedly scrawled in large letters, "*MEN IN HERE,*" on a board's rough surface. Then he climbed over the edge and squeezed past Duggan.

Shea and Bodenarek dumped a final box of sand into the frame. Wirta looked at Duggan and he nodded back. Holding a hammer he drove nails into the final lagging board to complete the bulkhead, leaving only a small hole against the wall. He twisted up his shirt into a wad and filled the hole.

"Okay, take that last timber across the top, and stretch the canvas tight as you can, side to side."

Wirta slit the last of the ventilation piping, separating it into sections. Duggan and Stewart nailed crossing planks into the timber set behind the first bulkhead. They stretched the canvas strips taut and carefully overlapped the edges, nailing them flat so the second canvas bulkhead was as close to airtight as possible, leaving a flap that could be pulled back to check the outer air.

"We got to check for gas leaks. Take turns, every hour."

They stepped back and held the lanterns up to inspect the face. Duggan leaned close, running his hands over the surface, holding his nose right against it, searching for any hint of smoke or gas. For long minutes he bent over and then slowly stretched up to the top, inspecting every inch. Finally he stepped back.

"She's tight."

***

Men lay in the dirt and rock. The waterboy had his head in his hands and stared at the lamps between the tracks. There was the soft click of rosary beads, mouths forming words.

Duggan looked at the men's faces and recognized many. He had delivered tools to most of them on the 24 and 26, out in the Snowball stopes. He tried to estimate the size of the sealed chamber, then counted the men, *Twenty-nine of us. Will there be enough air?*

Their gamble was set and he sat close to the bulkhead, keenly aware and suspicious of leaks.

"Open the air pipe," said Shea, "Even if there's a leak, gas can't get in if there's more pressure in here."

Stewart opened the valve. It gave a sharp hiss and immediately smoke and a sweet odor pervaded the air. "Damn, shut it off!" LaMontague shouted. "It's gas!"

Stewart hastily cranked it shut, but the odor lingered.

"Pipe must have cracked in the shaft, probably the heat," said Stewart.

"No," said Shea, explaining, "Pipe's got higher pressure, the gas can't get in the pipe – "

"Shut up," said LaMontague, cutting him off. "Just close the damn thing. That's the only way it don't leak."

"Ain't it still hissing?" asked Cobb.

"I can smell that damn stuff," cursed LaMontague, "Shut it closed."

"It's shut," Stewart said.

"I still hear it hissing.'"

"No, It's off."

They looked at the pipe with fear and suspicion. Duggan felt the mood and broke in, "We got air enough in here. Take turns and rap on the rails every few minutes. It'll tell rescuers we're here when they come looking."

He took his knife and hit the steel handle on a rail, three sharp hits, a pause, and three more, the metallic ring echoing down the track and into the mine.

"If they come," said Spihr morosely.

"They will," Duggan insisted. "Nobody leaves men deep. Sullau will be back."

"If he ain't dead."

Duggan looked at Spihr, a driller from the 2600, and put a hand on his shoulder, "Mike, we'll get out."

"Maybe it won't be a big fire," offered Shea.

Cobb looked up at him, "We was standing right there. Nothing to stop it burning the shaft, bottom to top," he said. "Might be worse than the Modoc."

A young man began singing with a soft brogue, almost to himself, his face scarcely whiskered. As he sang, one by one the other men stopped talking and listened.

Cobb and LaMontague tried to play cards, but after a few halfhearted hands, LaMontague tossed his down on the floor and Cobb put the deck away.

"You a gambler?" asked Cobb.

"Only when I have to," said LaMontague.

"I play to win," said Cobb.

The young singer's wistful voice trailed off and quiet filled the room.

Wirta looked at his watch. It was three in the morning on Saturday, June 9th.

CHAPTER FIFTEEN

BRALY STARTS THE RESCUE

Gathering rescuers, Braly sent the first teams down into the upper levels of the Speculator, and others tried to penetrate the workings from adjacent mines. But nobody could get any farther than the 800 foot level, crawling on hands and knees through smoke and steam, until the huge surface fans drove the poisoned air out.

By four in the morning, reports came in haphazardly, and Braly tried to make sense of them. Men had escaped through adjacent mines but not checked in. Nobody knew who was still underground. Bodies littered the drifts on the 600 and 700. At the 800 station, rescuers found men sprawled right at the door to the cage, succumbed to fumes before they could ring the signal bells. Fitzharris the shifter was among them. Men had been hoisted out of the Badger State unconscious. The entire lower shift of the Diamond had run to the Gray Rock and Corra workings. Three men had been overwhelmed and died within a few feet of the Diamond's 1800 station, including the mine manager, Big Con O'Neill.

On the 22 and 24 of the Speculator, men escaping to the High Ore had been stopped by concrete doors. Almost seventy men piled up, chased by gas, frantically pounding. The nipper Mulderig and a miner named James had the presence of mind to bring a pick and a sledge hammer. With panicking men pressed up behind them, they beat the concrete down. But those who had appeared at the surface told of dozens who had fled back into the workings to find another way, and now were perhaps trapped or dying.

On the surface, Braly began to understand what was happening below. Looking at the tag board, hundreds of tags still hung on the "in" side.

"Where are all those men?" Braly demanded.

"Nobody knows," said O'Keefe the timekeeper.

Counting up the tags, Braly sank into despair. By the time he counted two hundred there were still dozens more and he stopped, looking around the room at the rescuers. "This is nothing less than a catastrophe."

In the staging area of the mine office, a stern-faced Braly spoke to the head of rescue for the Anaconda Company, medical doctors, the mayor, and many volunteers, "Everybody in Butte's got a husband or brother, a father or uncle down there right now."

"I have to believe there are men alive. If we let the fire burn they'll die for sure. Their only chance is if we keep the fans reversed, bring the smoke up, and put the fire out."

Braly chewed over the ideas, "The deepest parts of the mine are already flooding. The pumps aren't working, the water's rising. If there are men down there..." He hesitated for long seconds, knowing his decision meant life for some and death for others. "Pour water down. Put the fire out."

As men filed out, he confided to his topman, Joe Barnicoat, "The only place live men can be is in the north country. We got to give anybody who's there more time to make it out. The rest of the mine is hell." Barnicoat nodded and Braly added, "I just pray I'm not wrong." He motioned, "Start the water."

The fire hoses had been dragged into position at the shaft. The smoke was so bad nobody could stand under the headframe without a helmet. Barnicoat yelled to the men at the hydrant across the yard. With the crank of a huge wrench, gusts of water pushed the hoses rigid, and a powerful stream shot down the shaft.

Water sprayed off the timbers and ran down the rock walls, free falling into the blackness and roiling smoke. It fell in rushes and sheets, splashing against the sides, down to levels a thousand, then two thousand feet below. When it hit the fire in the shaft, it hissed, misted and vanished. But as it continued to gush from above, cold water met superheated rock and the walls detonated as if dynamite were embedded in them. Burning timbers blasted loose, tremors rumbled through rock as explosions blew apart the shaft, caving it for hundreds of feet.

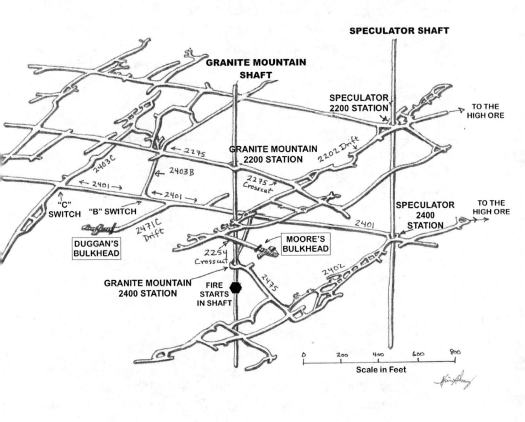

Moore's bulkhead in the 2254 and Duggan's in the 2471C

CHAPTER SIXTEEN

MOORE BEHIND THE BULKHEAD

Moore knew from the charred tang in the air around him that the gas had followed them in. He closed his eyes tightly.

"Crack the hose just a little," he ordered. Faces turned to Moore for assurance and he nodded. "Test the air."

A conspicuous haze hung in the lamp light. *We've got to take a chance for better air.*

Lisa lit a candle and held it near the end of the hose. The flame fluttered brightly and his face glistened in the candlelight, "She's fresh."

"Let's check for leaks in the wall," said Moore. Lisa took the candle to the bulkhead and worked with Moore, hunting for gas leaks. Each place the flame flickered lower, Moore slapped a handful of mud. They inched along, slowly passing the candle side-to-side until they had covered the entire wall.

Satisfied, Moore ordered, "Open the valve wide open. Keep it on as long as the air stays good."

The men gradually settled down, each finding a place against the walls surrounding the carbide lamps in the center.

Garrity whispered to Marthey, "You smell the smoke in here?"

"Yep."

"It's making me sick."

Truax asked, "What you think is going on?"

"Don't know," said Moore. "Could be the Modoc again, but seems worse. With the Modoc, we got to the shaft and were hoisted. Only a couple guys knocked out. Almost lost them, but nothing like this."

We might be in here a long time, Moore thought. He crouched naked in the lamp light and said, "Okay, lay anything you got here on the floor. Carbide? Matches? Candles?"

Truax slid three candles out of his pocket and put them in

132

the small pile. Moore nodded, "We'll use those to test the air."

Four men tossed little boxes of matches down, and their lamps, and several small cans of carbide. A little slower, out came cigarettes, a cigar, and tins of tobacco.

Moore took them, "No smoking," and tossed the tobacco to Sullivan. "Bury these."

Sullivan took the tobacco away from the bulkhead and scraped a hole in the crushed rock to bury it. Coming back, he tripped over a chunk of metal . "What's this?" he said and bent down, finding the broken end of a pipe. He followed it as it ran along the floor, then under the bulkhead. "We better check this."

"Put the candle to the open end," said Moore.

Lisa lowered it to the mouth of the pipe, the flame wavered and went out.

"Plug it up! Gas is coming through." Sullivan quickly packed mud into the end and they checked the floor again with the candle.

Moore felt the men's raw tension and tried to raise their spirits, saying confidently, "With the side drift, we got 100 feet of tunnel here, and the hose with pressure. We'll be good for air."

The men looked around, their eyes scanning the small space. Laszkeics' hand came up reflexively and touched his forehead, then his chest, as he silently mouthed, "In the name of the Father..." He caught himself and slowly put his hand down. Sullivan noticed and his eyes dropped. Nobody could face the fear welling up in all of them.

Moore took command of the bulkhead and lay down along the rails on the floor, "Rap every five or ten minutes. If rescuers hit on the rails or the pipe outside, we'll hear it."

Sullivan went to the back with Knutti and dug up fine clay from the pulverized rock under the drill, bringing it back to pile into small places to sit. The wetness of the floor soaked upward, and within minutes they sat in mud nests.

Moore reached to a small notch in the wall where he had placed his belongings, and took his pocket watch, a polished silver one that had been his father's. He broke the glass face, carefully picking off the shards so he could feel the hands and tell time in the dark. *For after the candles go out*, he thought. He felt the big hand at the top, and the hour hand near the bottom. "It's five o'clock," he joked to the others, "We're off shift."

Then he picked up his notebook and wrote a short letter to his wife in tight, simple lettering.

Dear Pet: This may be the last message you will get from me. The gas broke about 11:15. I tried to get all the men out, but the smoke was too strong. I got some of the boys with me in a drift and put in a bulkhead.
We have a $5000 life insurance policy, $3000 savings account in the bank. Those are yours. If anything happens to me, you had better sell the house and go to California and live.

Moore looked over the note and signed his full signature, *James D. Moore.*

Marthey sat next to him, "Boss, could you write a note for me?

"Sure, to who?"

"To my wife, she'll be worried."

Moore nodded, "What do you want to tell her?"

"That I'm here, that... and... uh, that..." Marthey struggled for words. "I don't know what to tell her," he said quietly.

"Here," Moore said, "How about, '... *I'll see you at home when this is over.*'"

"Yeah, that's okay."

Moore tore out the page and gave it to Marthey, who suddenly was near tears and nodded, "I got her and two little ones, a little boy that's two, a girl, she's three."

"Chin up," he said to Marthey, "we'll make it." Moore tapped the pencil on the cover of the notebook for a few minutes, then wrote another short note to his wife.

Dear Pet: 5 am. There is a young fellow here, Clarence Marthey, he has a wife and two kiddies.

Moore stopped writing and looked over at Marthey, who sat nervously folding and refolding the page Moore had given him. Then he put pencil to paper and finished slowly.

Tell her we done the best we could, but the cards were against us.

He leaned against the wall and thought, *I didn't get us out of the gas.*

Opening his notepad to a new page, he wrote again.

Dear Pet: Well, we are all waiting for the end. I guess it won't be long. We take turns rapping on the pipe, so if the rescue crew is around they will hear us.
My dear wife, try not to worry, I know you will but trust in God, everything will come out all right.
You will know your Jim died like a man and his last thought was for his wife that I love better than anyone on earth. We will meet again. Tell mother and the boys goodbye. With love to my Pet and may God take care of you.
Your loving Jim

Later the rock around them began to rumble and a pervasive grinding vibrated through the tunnel. It stopped briefly then started again, the timbers jiggling and squeaking. The shaking alarmed the men.

"What's that?" Sullivan asked, "They blasting?"

"Maybe the fire," said Moore reluctantly.

The sounds gradually died and the rumbling ceased, and they were left again in silence.

Shortly after, the hiss of the air hose softened. Moore nudged Garrity, "Check the air."

He turned over and put his hand up to the nozzle, "It's losing pressure."

They watched the hose in the flickering light. Moore finally said without any emotion in his voice, "That shaking, must have been the shaft caving in," he said. "It took the compressed air pipe out." He stopped and considered the implication. "Shut the valve,

135

we can't afford any gas coming through."

Sullivan said, "We don't have to stay here. I'll wet a shirt, hold it over my face and run for the shaft."

Moore fixed his eyes on Sullivan and said quietly, "It don't work like that Mike. You wouldn't get a hundred feet." Trying to keep the men's mood up, he added, "But we got a decent chance in here boys."

The air steadily became thicker, and the smells from the piss ditch mixed with the lingering smoke and poison gas that had infiltrated the chamber. They had shut themselves in with it, and it slowly worked on them, breath by breath as they used up the oxygen.

After another hour Marthey picked up one of the carbide lamps. He and Sullivan tried to light it until their thumbs were bruised. The flint threw sparks, but the lamp would not flame.

Sullivan tried to light a match in front of him. It made a dull snap and glowed, a trace of smoke floated around it. "Let me try another." The same thing happened, leaving a smudgy sulfur smell.

Moore watched. *Not enough oxygen to light a lamp*, he thought, angry at himself and their predicament. *If we could have just bulkheaded sooner…* He fought a growing despair, not wanting to admit what the failure of the hose meant. He had been depending on it for fresh air more than he dared accept. His thoughts whirled and clicked into place, leaving him staring grimly into the darkness. He took out his notepad and wrote again.

7 am. All alive, but air getting bad.
One small piece of candle left.

He watched his men's faces and read his notes. He could not rid himself of an increasing sense of dread.

Wax from the candle stub dripped steadily down on the muddy floor, until only the blackened wick balanced upright in a small molten puddle, hardening around the mud edges. The wick fell over with a tiny *pfhsst*, and absolute darkness enveloped them.

Moore sat looking at the bright afterimage left in his eyes. He opened his notebook and carefully spelled out a few words, the pencil making precise little scrapes on the paper. He ran his fingers over the page trying to judge where his pencil was on the paper, then added a final sentence.

9 am. In the dark.
Think it is all off.

He set the notebook carefully down beside him. Now, with no light, the men could not see him and he stopped hiding the pain in his chest.

CHAPTER SEVENTEEN

SULLAU'S SACRIFICE

Sullau leaned on the broken opening watching Felutovich's lantern disappear into the Badger's tunnels, then turned and climbed back through the shattered bulkhead. Somewhere back in the Speculator north country were Bronson and the other men.

With the bulkhead down, the air currents swept through the crosscut and pulled smoke and gas from the Granite Mountain shaft into the Badger. It came through in waves, thicker, then clearing.

Sullau held his useless handkerchief over his mouth, stumbling into the haze with his lantern up. He was dazed and losing balance, suffocating from the inside as the carbon monoxide poisoned his blood. A few hundred feet further, the drift met with the main crosscut.

He heard muffled voices and saw a feeble glow ahead.

"Jack!" he yelled.

"Here!" came the answer. Sullau crept along and yelled again. Bronson called back, closer now.

Feeling along the rock wall, the rough surface opened into a drift on the left side. Stepping around the corner, he saw two lanterns burning low and the outlines of Bronson, McFadden, and several others. He edged into the space and dropped to the floor.

In the dim light, Bronson motioned to him. The other men lay with their faces to the ground below the heaviest smoke.

"Get down. Better air."

Sullau weakly crawled over. "Why didn't you come?" he asked Bronson. "I got the others to the Badger."

"The gas came too strong," Bronson said, and gestured at the drift they sat in, "We found better air here. Must be a raise connecting this drift to the Rainbow."

Sullau looked at him, unable to understand the words, "How's that?"

"There's a draft pushing the gas out. This fresh air has to be coming from the Rainbow." Bronson said and looked at Sullau closely, thinking, *Ernest is in trouble.*

The men peered into the crosscut, they could see waves of smoke push by. Sullau sat up, leaning against the wall, but his head fell forward onto his chest and his breathing faltered. The gas had stolen his strength.

Sullau had been fighting to help the men since he started the fire. He jerked awake and guilt tightened his heart. Turning to Bronson, he fumbled to find words. "Don't know whether it was my lamp or Collins'," he said.

"What?" Bronson looked at him, not understanding his meaning.

Futility cut through him like a damned soul. "The fire," he willed himself to say, "It's my fault."

The carbide flame fluttered. A cool breeze came from the darkness behind them, pushing into the drift. A few mica shards became visible, glittering on the opposite wall of the drift.

"Smoke's lighter," said Bronson.

"Maybe we break for it," offered McFadden.

Sullau pulled himself to his feet, saying, "This is our chance for the Badger." The others struggled off the ground, following his flickering lamp out of the drift.

They had gone no more than a hundred feet when dense smoke swept through the tunnel again. McFadden could not see, and put his hand on Sullau's back. Sullau was fading, his feet began to drag, then he stopped and half-turned toward Bronson.

"Catch me," he gasped weakly, "I can't go any further..." and collapsed onto the floor of the tunnel beyond Bronson's reach.

Bronson and McFadden grabbed Sullau under his arms, and together they dragged him. Murphy and McMurray picked up his legs, and the four men shuffled forward with the big man hanging unconscious in their arms, his hands limp and scraping the ground.

Murphy tripped, and the group went down hard. Two of the lanterns went out, the third flickered weakly on its side. Bronson hit his head on the track, stunned for a few moments before he rose slowly up on all fours.

139

The men labored to their feet. Sullau lay unconscious, face down in the mud, his breathing hoarse and ragged. "I'll carry him," said McFadden.

They hoisted Sullau up, balancing him on McFadden's broad shoulders. Bronson retrieved his lamp and moved in front, showing the way. McFadden staggered 20 steps down the crosscut, then 30, 40, but lost control of his legs and collapsed.

Bronson looked at Sullau's vacant face, eyes closed. "Ernest..."

Murray gasped, "We got to leave him."

"I can't," said Bronson.

Murray urgently pulled at Bronson's arm, "We'll die if we stay."

Bronson looked down at Sullau. He grasped his friend by collar and shook him. "Sully!"

"Jack, come on!" screamed Murray.

They left Sullau and crawled on all fours along the rails. A choking nightmare pressed in on them. Then a voice called out, "Bronson, in here!"

Bronson crawled toward the voice with his face close to the ground. He reached out and his fingers told him there was an opening on the side of the drift and crawled into it, the others right behind him.

Cooler air flowed around them and he could see the dim form of a man lying down. In the back there was a winz, a chute feeding fresh air from a higher level. One after another the four men crawled into the space and rested there, panting, lungs shouting for air.

On his elbows, Bronson held his lantern up and the light shone on a man's face, "Cozanne," said Bronson. Pete Cozanne, one of Bronson's miners from the 2400, lying near the wall.

"Good air," said Cozanne. "Been here for a while."

Bronson sprawled full length on the ground, panting in clean air from an open chute behind. It washed over them, pressing the smoke back, and he thought he could hear faint rasping breaths back in the crosscut.

"We're in Badger country," said Cozanne, "This air is coming through their upper levels."

A metal air pipe carrying compressed air hung on the wall, and McFadden began rapping on it, hoping somebody from the Badger might hear. After some time, the scrape of bootsteps came up the drift, unseen in the smoke, and Bronson called out, "Over here!"

A muffled call came back, "How she going?"

Men appeared with tanks and breathing tubes, goggles set like blank eyes into their canvas head gear. Bronson motioned, "Sullau's back on the tracks. Get him, quick as you can." The men returned in a few minutes, dragging his body.

"Is he alive?" asked Bronson.

"Heart beating. But looks bad."

They lay him down in the clean air, and Bronson crawled over and held his friend's face and gently called to him, "Ernest, wake up." He put his head on Sullau's chest and listened, the heart beat was faint, but he thought he could hear it.

"Anybody else close?" asked the rescuers.

"Don't know," McFadden said.

Bronson kept rubbing Sullau's face and patting his cheeks softly, "Don't die, Ernest."

"We're getting you to safety," the rescuers said, and steadied Bronson and the others to their feet. They lifted Sullau onto a rail truck and wheeled him to the station. Somebody rang the signal bells.

At the surface in the Badger mineyard, doctors carefully lifted Sullau and Bronson watched the barrage of working hands on his friend. He was stunned by the fresh air and the people scurrying around him. He followed as the doctors carried Sullau to the main office, pleading silently, *God have mercy on him.*

He sat down on a pile of stacked timbers. Men rushed through the yard, the topman shouted orders. Another group came off the cages, escaping from the Speculator led by rescuers, drained from their battle through the drifts. Bronson stood up, intending to walk over to them, but his balance faltered and he lay back down on the timbers in the cold air. Somebody cast a coat over him, and exhaustion carried him away.

In the east the sky lightened, silhouetting the jagged outline of the Divide mountains, hinting at the coming dawn.

When he woke, Sullau was dead.

CHAPTER EIGHTEEN

DUGGAN'S BULKHEAD

Saturday 8:45 am. Have been here since 12:00 Friday night. No gas coming through the bulkhead. Have plenty of water. All in good spirits.
Duggan

Duggan sat against the wall, holding a stub of a pencil and putting notes on a small folded piece of paper.

"What you writing?" asked Cobb.

"A letter to me wife, Madge."

"Hmm, Manus and Madge..." Cobb said, "She a beauty?"

Duggan shot a little smile. "Yeah, Tussy," calling Cobb by his nickname, "pretty as I ever saw."

Cobb stuck him with an elbow, "Always thought you must be pleasing to the ladies."

He laughed, "Nah, her mom ran a little boarding house and I moved in, working in the mines. Never paid her mind, just a kid. But she grew up, and a nice-looking young lady. Tougher than me. Spunky. Said later she had her eye on me."

"Never know what's going on in a woman's mind."

"Got married last year. Building a house now." His voice turned soft, "She's due in July."

Cobb let out a long breath, "Aye, me as well, a wife and mother. On Wyoming Street."

Cobb turned and looked at LaMontague. "You married?"

"Wedding's on Monday, in Missoula," LaMontague said softly, his eyes half shut. "That's where she's from. We've been saving and we'll buy a house, one on the north side."

The men were quiet for a time, nursing their own thoughts.

Still lying down, LaMontague asked, "Manus, how we going to get out of here?"

"Climb, if the gas lets up."

"Where? Can we get up the Spec?"

"The hoist wasn't going below the 2000. They had a bulkhead across the shaft. We'd have to find a manway in the Edith May, climb maybe four hundred feet, and hope we didn't get tangled up in the gas. It's not a good way."

LaMontague opened his eyes and sat up, "The manways were full of smoke. Cobb couldn't make it, or Wirta."

Duggan answered, "Yeah, I don't think we could do it. We can try the Spec station. But you know, if the hoist ain't running, then we should go out the Rainbow. Climb the 2439C manway."

"Never been. Where is it?"

"Snowball stopes, eight hundred feet from here. Take the B switch and go to the right. It starts just north of the crosscut."

Recognition flickered on LaMontague's face, "The B switch?"

"That's the next one out, goes past the Gem shaft."

"Think there's gas?"

Duggan shrugged, "Don't know. But it's the most likely to be clear the whole way. You go right by the Gem, then toward the Rainbow. The upcasts will pull the smoke out."

"What about the Badger? Or the High Ore?"

"The drifts were filled with smoke." Duggan leaned to LaMontague, "Best bet is out the B switch to the Snowball drifts, then climb up."

"How far?"

"Maybe a mile."

Sitting back from the inner canvas wall, Cobb saw Duggan writing again but could not make out the words.

"Manus, what you writing now?"

Duggan leaned forward and whispered softly so none of the other men could hear, "My will. If the worse comes, it'll make things easier for Madge. Here, if you want to write something ..." he offered the pad of paper to Cobb.

Cobb recoiled. "I can't write my will," he said. "It's like ... planning to die."

Duggan shrugged, "Tussy, it's God's will if we die or not."

"Well, I ain't going to write it anyhow," said Cobb, "I'm going to live."

144

They had been sealed in rock for eighteen hours, and the men stared at the lantern flame and the damp hot air lay heavy around them. Shea stopped rapping on the pipe. "There's no damn point making noise," he said despondently. "They ain't coming."

"It'll take time to clear out the levels," said Duggan, "so they can get down here."

Shea hit the rail once, hard, and cursed. "If it takes much more, ain't none of us going to be left to welcome them."

"Might be up to us to get out," said Cobb.

"Check the gas again, see if it's cleared," said Shea.

Duggan pulled the shirt out of the small hole and smelled it. He quickly stuffed it back in. "Still gas," he said. He felt the men's eyes on him, hope diminishing. "They'll come," he assured them.

"Damned if they will," muttered Shea below his breath. "Damn it all."

The chamber trailed off into a dull silence, wearing them down. The harsh reality softened, and for a time they fell into merciful unconsciousness. Nobody rapped the rails or listened for noises from the other side of the wall.

***

Duggan woke confused, *Had somebody been outside the wall?* He had trouble focusing his thoughts. Hurriedly, he picked up his knife off the floor and started hitting the rail. Three sharp raps, pause, and then three more. He knocked on the wooden planks, using the end of the crowbar, and wakened Stewart who lay down next to him, "Eh? Manus, what?"

"We haven't been making any noise. If somebody comes, they won't know we're here."

"Ahh," Stewart waved at him, "probably be a day before anybody can get down to this level. Nobody would risk it, even with a helmet."

145

But the feeling lingered and Duggan hit the rails again. McAdams joined him, and for the next hour they took turns every few minutes until their hands ached.

***

Doubts rose to disillusionment, then anger. Underneath was a growing fear that nobody would say. "We should run for it," came a whisper. With increasingly distrustful tones, the men became irritable, watching the bulkhead with suspicion.

A Serb named Evcovich screamed and lurched to his feet, yelling and stumbling over the other men, "Break wall!"

Duggan sat up, and Shea whispered to him, "Is he really going try to break the bulkhead?"

Evcovich shuffled closer. Shea curled his hand into a fist. Duggan nudged Shea, "See what he does."

The man stumbled over heads, arms and legs, and men weakly warded him away, "Lie down!" yelled a voice.

"Jesus, my head...", said another.

He fell on several men and they roughly shoved him into the center of the tunnel, and he lay gasping and muttering. Guarding the bulkhead, Duggan listened for a few minutes until all had quieted.

***

The air became thicker and the men's thinking more sluggish. Near midnight Duggan woke and felt dazed for a time until he realized, *We're using up our air. We've got to blow out the lamps.* "Turn off the lamps!" said Duggan.

Men roused themselves and grumbled.

"What you saying?" Negretto demanded.

Duggan began to answer, but one of the Serbs put his burly arms around his lamp, snarling. Other voices raised in angry defiance, "No!"

Duggan insisted, "We're running out of air, we have to shut some of them off."

146

"This is mine!" said a man.

Duggan didn't answer. The men's faces were angry, their shoulders hunched, like fearful animals backed into a corner. He knew he could be outnumbered, and gauged carefully what to say next. His voice rang across the chamber, "Would you rather have light to see, or air to breath?"

The question hung there. The Serb looked at his lamp, then around the room and back to Duggan. The certainty in his eyes wavered. McAdams picked his lamp up and blew it out. One by one, other men did the same. The Serb continued to hold his lamp distrustfully, his hands shaking.

"We have to do this," said Duggan.

The Serb's lips trembled, then he snuffed out his lamp. Four of the carbide lamps were left.

***

Duggan put back the shirt, "Doesn't seem so bad out there, maybe it's clearing."

"Air's God-awful in here," said Cobb, "Let's break a little hole at the top."

They stood, and at the top of the wall Duggan forced out a board. Cobb chipped out the packed dirt with a drill bit.

"Careful, keep it small," warned Duggan.

Cobb tapped lightly and the drill bit popped through. Cooler air came in. For a few minutes, the foul air went out and the air in the bulkhead seemed better, then the smoke came strong again.

"Close it off." They quickly crammed the hole with dirt.

"Maybe the air's better near the floor."

They picked at the bottom part of the wall with the bit until it opened a small hole near the floor. Duggan got down on all fours, his nose to the ground, "Damn! Plug it up! It's terrible out there."

They stuffed rags back in and sat down dejected, backs to the bulkhead. *We're running out of air*, Duggan thought to himself. *How long will it take for the gas outside to clear?*

By one o'clock Sunday morning, the men fought to breath. Duggan told the group, "Turn out all but one lamp. We've got to save air." One after the other, three flames disappeared, until only one remained with twenty-nine men staring at it. Duggan did not say anything aloud, but everyone worried that it might be too late. In the shadows he took out his pad and wrote briefly, then crossed himself furtively, so the others would not see.

Sunday 1 am. I realize that all oxygen has been consumed. Everybody breathing heavily. If death comes it will be caused by all oxygen used from the air in the chamber.
Duggan

A small-framed man stirred. He knelt and stretched his hands upwards and began praying out loud. His face was open and beseeching, his chest bare. He spoke low and pled what was in their hearts, "God, if You are above us, as we are told You are, look down on me and my friends. Save us. God, please be good to us."

The lone lantern sat on the empty dynamite box and lit the room for another hour, dim and ghostlike. Their eyes were drawn to it, absorbed in every flicker. It sputtered, pulsing then fading until it was barely visible, a drop of transparent yellow.

Cobb held his breath as he watched the demise of the flame, like a fading heartbeat. It lowered again, smaller and smaller. Finally it gave a little pop and was gone, leaving them in the pure blackness. His throat tightened and the men sank into despair.

***

Cobb tried lighting a lantern. A few sparks flew, but that was all. Shea tried striking matches, which glowed red and went out without a sound.

Their lips were swollen and pasted together, with only a few drops of water left to wet their mouths. Negretto's tongue stuck to his teeth, slurring the words he tried to say. Fowler lay on the floor fanning his face, as if the moving foul air had more life than the black stillness filling their chamber.

One of the men woke screaming, "Da mine is fire!" Sounds of scraping and movement, he crawled panic-stricken, swearing and striking, past Shea toward Duggan. Other voices joined him through the chamber shouting, "We go!"

Duggan didn't raise his voice, but assured them, "Not yet. There's still gas out there."

They sputtered angrily in broken English, but Duggan's voice came back, "You won't make it."

"We go out!"

"You're certain of death. You can't outrun the gas."

Cobb whispered to Shea, "Take them if they try to break the wall." He and Shea tensed, readying for a fight to save everybody in the drift.

But the spell of Duggan's voice floated through the darkness, "It will clear. Then we'll leave."

There was silence. Cobb picked up a crowbar. Duggan nudged Shea, "Rap on the pipe, tell them rescuers will come." Shea hit it slowly, and the sharp ring cut the dark.

Grit stuck to their bodies, mud on their legs, they were bound into the chamber. From back in the group a man blurted out, "We're dying in here!" Other voices rang out frightened in the dark, men at the brink of breakdown. "Let's take our chances outside." A chorus of ayes croaked and a smattering of nays. A man shouted to Duggan, "Get out of the way."

Duggan rose to his feet and stood before the bulkhead. "Boys, we got to be game. In here's our only chance," he said.

"I say run for it!" yelled the voice, and others called out, "Get out of the way! Better death in the gas than here in a hole."

"If you break this wall down, you won't make it and you'll kill the rest of us." Duggan pulled the shirt out of the bulkhead and waved it, "Smell this." The shirt reeked of gas and the smell penetrated the dark. The shouting men went silent.

"They'll come for us," Duggan added. "You have my word."

The flare of emotions died down, and across the chamber men lay exhausted. *He's got the best brain of all us*, thought Shea.

149

Time ebbed on. Shea scribbled a note:

No water to drink, nothing to eat. Foul air. The carbide lamps, the candle don't work. My matches won't light, and they're good matches. Men getting desperate, some of the fellows crazy, want to burn up the bulkhead, commit suicide. Can't stand the suffering. We've rapped on the pipe and made out there was somebody coming, we rapped a million times. It's all fake, nobody will ever show.

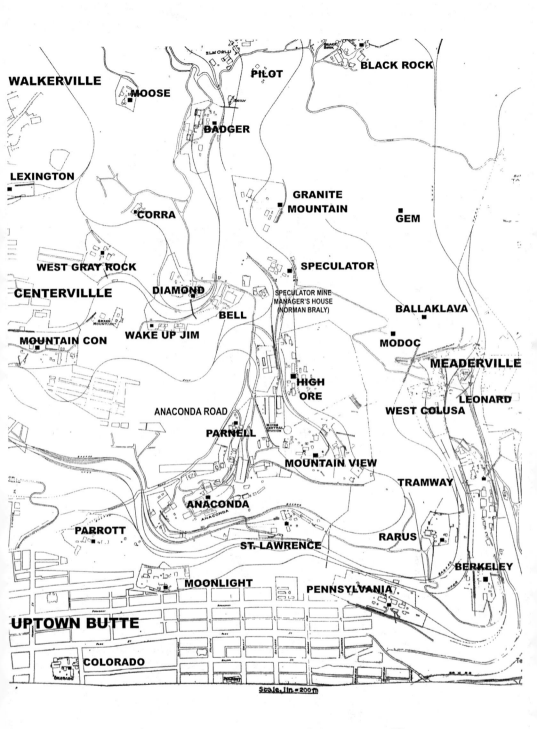

Mines on the East side of the Butte Hill.

CHAPTER NINETEEN

UNDERGROUND SEARCH INTENSIFIES

When the fire first began, the night shift bosses did their damnedest to get their men out, any way they could. They knew the mine better than anyone else and after getting their own men to safety, they went back in to help, joined by men who had helmet training.

Big Jack Hamill, the boss from the 1800, guided his men through the north country to the Badger, then ran back over to the Speculator mineyard. Bosses Weigenstein and Goodell were already on the surface and the three grabbed helmets and descended repeatedly into the mine to search for living men. More rescuers appeared at the headframe, drawn by the whistles and telephone calls. The mineyard teemed with activity.

By two in the morning Braly had taken over the command. Men from the Anaconda and Tramway rescue teams, the Poulin and others showed up, volunteering for trips to any level.

After the first light of morning Camits and Boyce appeared alive from the 700, and hope was renewed. Other men struggled to adjacent mine shafts and were raised far away from the Speculator. Reports of what was happening underground were chaotic. Dozens of men from all over the mine reported that Sullau had showed them how to escape. He seemed to have been everywhere in the mine. But around five in the morning, word came from the Badger that he had been brought to the surface unconscious and had died leading another group out.

By full daylight, all of the shift bosses had been down multiple times. They wore the awkward breathing apparatus into the heat, darkness, and gas, and lifted out the bodies of men they recognized and whose families they knew. As the hours went by, they realized that five of their fellow shift bosses were missing.

The initial frenzy wore off and the exhaustion mounted, until the night shift men were running on sheer determination.

Goodell stumbled while putting on a new set of tanks, and Hamill came over, "Luther, you're done in."

"Get out of my way," said Goodell, trying to push past Hamill onto the cage.

Hamill blocked him. "You should rest."

"Moore's down there," said Goodell, looking hollow-eyed. "Nobody's seen him."

Hamill would not budge. "Let the other men take over or we'll be dragging your body out too."

Braly was joined by Boardman, the head of Anaconda rescue, and together they organized the underground search like an army campaign, with crews moving level by level, drift by drift, deeper into the mine. The crews lowered down the Speculator shaft or entered through the connections from the Badger in the north and the High Ore in the south, each with a specific set of places to explore.

The strong draft from the ventilation fan pushed from above, clearing the upper levels. But below 1600, teams stepped off into a murky darkness, lamps haloed in the gloomy smog. Everything was blanketed by fine black ash.

The rescuers formed relays, those with only thirty-minute air supplies brushed off faces and tried to identify men, then raised them up the shaft. Those with the larger helmets went into the drifts, gone for two hours at a time as they systematically combed the tunnels.

At eleven in the morning, water had been cascading down the Granite Mountain shaft for five hours and put out the upper levels of the fire, but it still burned hot below the 1800. The partial quenching increased the smoke, now mixed with sweltering steam. As they searched, rescuers entered a reeking miasma that burned their faces and extinguished their lamps. Two men's helmets had malfunctioned. Falling unconscious, they had to be dragged out and revived at the surface.

Starting at the 1800, the mine tunnels became more complex. Crosscuts from the deeper stations ran far into the north country, to the Croesus, Snowball, and Berlin veins a half-mile from

153

the Speculator shaft. To reach them, helmet men had to go ever farther from safety.

Volunteers crowded around the mine office, shouting their willingness to head down into hell, but only those who were trained were allowed onto the rescue teams. With all the intense action in the mineyard, people forgot that underground, one simple mistake with the breathing apparatus could be their death.

Standing in front of the full group of rescuers, Braly warned, "No matter which way you go in, you'll have a long way underground. You only have two hours of air. Go over all your equipment carefully. A malfunction can kill you. You won't be able to turn around and get out fast enough."

After he was finished with the group, Braly took Rosie Smith of the Tramway team and shift boss Budelier aside, "You're going into the 24 next?"

Budlier nodded, "Yeah, Frink and Boardman want that checked."

Rosie broke in, "I was on the 24, and we heard what sounded like rapping on the rails and pipes. Couldn't tell where it came from. Started and stopped, couldn't get a bead. We need to check that out, might be men trapped."

Braly rolled out the stope map, "Where were you?"

Smith scanned the tunnels, "Here," he pointed just north of the Speculator shaft, "where the crosscut from the Granite Mountain station hits the 2401."

"What should I check?" asked Budelier.

"The rapping could have come from the Jessie or Lynchburg stopes, maybe further. This area," Braly pointed to the Croesus. "This B switch area where the drifts split."

"We have to work through the levels as fast as we can," he said. "Look in the north country, it's our best hope to find living men."

The team suited up and Budelier called his men around him. Pointing to the stope map he said, "We're starting a thousand feet from the Spec, and we'll go on the connecting tunnel, past the shaft on the 2401. That will take us north. We'll check all the drifts we can. Keep an eye on your watches, we'll turn around when there's thirty minutes left."

They descended the High Ore shaft, making their way to the temporary brattice that had been erected between the mines to hold the smoke back. Budelier had been on shift fifteen hours, and this was his fourth trip of the day.

"Remember boys, Rosie said it's bad enough that you can go unconscious in less than a minute. If you have any trouble with your helmet, give three tugs, wave your arms," he said soberly. "We're a team of six, if one has trouble, we all go back."

They checked their helmets and cleaned their goggles. He motioned to the High Ore men who turned on the fan, pressurizing the tunnel and the brattice that kept the Speculator's smoke out of the High Ore. The men swung the door open, when Budelier's team moved past, it snapped shut behind them.

They were met by a murk of smoke and steam. The surface fans had changed the air flow, forcing it up the Granite Mountain shaft, but there was still heavy smoke feeding into these levels. The normal temperature was eighty-five degrees, but now it was sweltering. After several minutes of walking, they reached the concrete bulkhead that had been broken down by the men escaping from the Speculator.

They moved along the tunnels from the High Ore into the Speculator workings, past the shaft and turned into the north county. Visibility was almost nil, and each had one hand on the shoulder of the man in front of him. There were short runs where timbers and posts were stored, and the powder room, but no signs of men. They continued along the main tunnel until they reached the crosscut over to the Granite Mountain station.

Budelier motioned to the others, *Turn left here.*

As they walked toward the station, from the Granite Mountain shaft came the sounds of granite chunks cracking loose and rumbling as stations above caved in and ricocheted downward. Nearing the shaft, the fire-scorched rock radiated heat, and in front of them, burning timbers cracked and hissed.

They stopped just before reaching the station on the 2400. The metal turnsheets had buckled up from the floor by the heat.

Rails were bent at sharp right angles where they touched the sheets, and broken pipes rattled in the shaft. The destruction of the station was complete, the mine was a wasteland.

Budelier shook his head and pointed backwards to leave, *There are no men here.*

They turned around, walked out to the main 2401 crosscut, and turned again into the north country. Behind them, irregular noises persisted, sounding like a boiler hissing, steel wheels spinning haphazardly, the sounds of a dying mine. As they walked farther the noises receded, but now and again a sharp sound rang along the rails or the water pipes, and reverberated down the drifts.

They checked the Jessie and Lynchburg drifts but found nothing. Farther on the main 2401, there was a new tunnel cut due north to meet the Croesus vein. The drillers were still crosscutting and the tunnel was undeveloped. Budelier remembered the number, 2471C.

Budleier took his mouthpiece out and said to the others, "We'll check this." As they entered, the smoke became more dense. The push from the ventilation fans had not reached the air in this dead-end. Budelier looked at his watch and, even with his lamp up close, he had trouble reading it. He led two men, Crowley and Whitmore, as they fumbled along touching the walls, their lamps burning a dull orange.

The rails ended abruptly, going under a wall built of timbers. He had expected to find a drill at a crosscutting face, not a wooden wall. Above their heads, a compressed air pipe hung in the upper corner of the drift. It too went through the wall. He strained to remember the stope map, *Where did this tunnel end?* He tapped the wall. It was solid, with thick chute planks and lagging nailed firmly into the timber set. *They must have wanted this to stay in place.*

An air pipe but no drill? he thought, *what were the drilling crews doing in here?* The earlier team had said they heard rapping in this area, but Budelier had not heard anything. He put his hand on the pipe and listened. All he could hear was the hiss of his oxygen regulator, and the hoarse sound of his own breaths in the tubes of his apparatus. When he brought his lamp up near his face to look at the wall, the dense smoke made it impossible to see more than a few inches. He felt around, his hands passed Cobb's message scratched on the boards, "*MEN IN HERE.*" It was covered with soot, and no one noticed.

Crowley tugged at his arm, then held his watch close to Budelier's goggles. In the dim lamplight, he could just make out the hands, *two minutes to eight.* Crowley mumbled through the mouthpiece, "We got eighteen minutes of air left." Budelier pulled at Whitmore's shoulder, motioning with his hand, "We have to go back." They turned and began retracing their steps.

With their lamps barely burning, they shuffled down the drift to the main crosscut and headed back toward the Speculator shaft. The steam thickened and Budelier covered his neck, squinting through his goggles, sweat streaming down his body. He was breathing hard, and the hiss of the air hoses filled his ears. Then he noticed a different noise and stopped to listen. High-pitched and quick. *Was that three raps?* It seemed to ring along the rail. He held his breath, trying to sense what direction it came from, but it did not continue.

Whitmore tapped his watch urgently. They were far behind where they should be. *Only ten minutes left, fourteen hundred feet to the High Ore.* Just enough air to make it back to safety. Frustrated, Budelier gave up on the noise and they walked as quickly as possible. By the time they passed the Speculator shaft their lamps burned brighter and they could walk without feeling their way.

Finally they reached the brattice at the High Ore. Budelier beat on it and took his mouthpiece out, yelling, "Open up!"

The men behind shoved it open and a blast of air from a ventilation fan welcomed him. Three of his men crowded through, followed by Crowley, Whitmore, and Budelier, and the door slammed shut behind them.

"Glad to see you," he said to the man, who handed him a canteen. He swilled the water and spat it out on the floor, washing the bitterness of the rubber mouthpiece away, then drank deeply.

"Find anyone?" asked the High Ore man.

Budelier looked down and spat again, "Nothing. Nobody."

***

On the surface, Braly walked through the Speculator's temporary morgue with a heavy heart, looking at the canvas-covered figures lying on the floor, thanking the workers and volunteers. He uncovered Sullau's body and gazed at his friend. His eyes were closed, his face still full and strong. Braly had the overwhelming feeling that the powerful man would rise up and brush himself off, then head back to his shift. But the figure remained still.

It was more than Braly could bear. He whispered, "I would have liked to shake your hand one more time." He said a quiet goodbye as Sullau was taken away.

Briefly, he stepped back into his office and closed the door, reading and re-reading the note Sullau had written to him after the cable had fallen. "My God, Ernest," he said quietly, "How did this happen?"

Folding the paper carefully, he put it in his pocket and went back out the door into the madness.

Members of the Tramway Rescue Team wearing their Draeger helmet
apparatus ready to go into the Speculator during the disaster.
Anaconda Standard June 12, 1917, *Butte Miner* June 11, 1917.
Used with permission from Butte-Silver Bow Archives.

CHAPTER TWENTY

FAMILIES ON THE SURFACE

Throughout the night word spread to the families whose men worked in the Speculator, neighbors knocked on doors and party lines rang. Lights came on and did not go out as people tried to push back the growing terror.

By daybreak a darkness rose on the hill like a dirty fountain, flooding the slopes, over buildings, and into the streets of the city. The sky closed in, and a spring snowstorm swept across the city, swirling together snow, smoke, and ash. People stepped out of their homes, troubled, sensing ruin from deep in the earth.

By eight in the morning on Saturday, a crowd of men, women and children gathered at the closed front gates of the mine. Security guards were posted and only those with official business were allowed in. The line continued to grow until the entire area outside of the yard was filled with people trying to get word, any word, of their loved ones under the ground.

They peered through cracks in the fence to catch a glimpse of what was going on in the yard. Young men climbed the wooden headframe that stood outside the gate and kept watch, calling from time to time to describe the action around the shaft. Anguish grew heavier as every miner carried out from the cages was lifeless. A group of doctors waited and looked for even a glimmer of life that they might work to save.

From time to time, haggard men straggled over from the adjacent mines, having escaped and been hoisted up the Badger, Diamond, or High Ore, now looking for their friends and family. Finding a wife or son, or the family seeing the father, groups dissolved into tears of relief, as those around them waited and prayed that their own men would appear.

The guards at the Speculator gates were besieged with cries, "Please tell me if my husband is alive." The guards did their best to reason with the women, some who were neighbors and friends and called them by name.

160

The watchman collected information from people at the gate. "Please write down the names and I will give them to the time keepers." Within a few minutes dozens of scribbled notes were thrust at him, *Jack Gamwells, Matt Hill, Chris Vokovich...*, names and addresses penciled on scraps of cardboard and torn-off margins of newspapers. The guard brought the armful of notes back to the office where the timekeepers McDonald and O'Keefe were and set them in a pile on the table, "These are from the folks outside. Can you figure out which of these men have been identified, and which are missing?"

The weary timekeepers nodded, "It'll be on the next list."

They sent a man from the mine office to give updates. The guards opened the ten foot high wooden gate, and he squeezed into the opening to address the crowd, reading a prepared statement. "Rescue work is centered on the 600 through 800. We hope to be into the 1800 foot level by mid-afternoon. Many men escaped and have been raised from other mines. We don't know all their names yet. We just got word that a group of eight made it to the Mountain Con. So far, we've found twenty-four men who didn't survive."

The murmurs of the crowd grew, and he raised his voice. "Please check nearby mines and at home. Your men may have gone there and not here. The lists of those accounted for and those identified will be updated as we can."

The order of the crowd broke down as he finished. Wives clamored with fear, people shouted questions at him, and all he could do was wave and retreat. "I'm sorry, I don't know any more."

Back inside he told O'Keefe, "I thought they were going to tear me apart..."

***

The wind came up and clouds shuttered the sun, twisting the smoke and pushing it across the upper ridge of the hill. In a lull, an older woman stood in the road before the gate to the mineyard, wearing a simple faded dress and a threadbare coat. A chill breeze cut through the crowd and people shivered. With hair streaming out and blown by the wind, her voice lifted and pleaded,

161

praying with her arms raised, "O God, please Dear God, save my husband, save my two sons."

Her face streamed with tears as she knelt in the road, beseeching the sky.

IDENTIFIED DEAD

JACK GAMWELLS, 133 Pacific, shift boss, aged 41, wife and two children.

NEIL DOHERTY, 69 East Copper, 46, married.

MAURICE FITZHARRIS, 607 South Main, 47, married, four children.

ERNEST SULLAU, 2302 Wall street, assistant foreman, married.

JOHN J. BRADY, 126 East Park street, 30, single.

WILLIAM RAMSEY, 445A South Ohio street, 30, single.

CHRIS VUKOVICH, 319 East Woolman.

JOHN M'GINNIS, 201 Toboggan avenue, Walkerville, 39, married.

TONY IVICICH, 345 East Mercury, 33, married.

YOUNG LINDSTED, 645 South Main, 25, single.

ERIC OLING, 540 East Broadway, 25, single.

KELLY ROBERTS, contractor.

MIKE CONROY, 966 South Utah.

PETER SHERIDAN, 616 East Galena.

GEORGE THOMAS, 724 North Wyoming, 26, married, wife and three children.

GEORGE JANICICH, 9 Duggan avenue, 27, single.

JEFF PERRY, 9 Seal terrace, 27, married.

RICHARD VOGEL, 129 West Copper, 50, married.

VICTOR S. SHAFFORD, 540 South Main (first shift), 25, single.

WILFRED ST. JACQUES, 87 East Front, 48, single.

TOM GARRITY, 213 North Idaho street.

CON O'NEILL, Bell mine, foreman, married.

EDWARD LOWREY, 21 East Center street, Centerville.

ALBERT H. DE BOER, 703 East Galena street, 25, single.

JACOB JACOBSON, 1122 East Park street, 23, single.

VERNON THOMPSON, 322 North Montana street, 19, single.

MATT HILL, Anaconda road, 40, wife and two children.

Identified Dead, *Anaconda Standard*, June 10, 1917
Used by permission of Butte-Silver Bow Archives.

163

CHAPTER TWENTY-ONE

THE NEWSPAPER BOY

Matt stepped inside his home to the smell of a warm dinner. For an instant, he had the feeling that his wife would come around the corner, laughing, telling him of all the things the children had done during the day. But Mina had passed away more than a year before, and now it was just him and the children. His youngest son yelled from above "Pa!", and three boys bounded down the stairs, pushing each other out of the way.

The oldest came to a stop before colliding with his father, who was hanging up his jacket in the foyer. The younger ones stayed on the stairs looking over their big brother's shoulders.

"What a greeting!" said Matt. "Smells great in here!"

"Sis is making supper," said the youngest. "And William is here."

Matt tousled the boy's hair, "Well, then we should pay our respects." He hung up his jacket, put his arms around two of the boys, and they turned into the dining room.

Matt's daughter stood up from the table with the young man. She smiled self-consciously at her father, then shushed her brothers who lingered behind, teasing her. William set his glass on the table and held out his dusty hand to Matt.

Linda had taken over the household duties at seventeen after her mother had died, but she had her own interests too. William had come to Butte looking for work. He was twenty-two, the same age Matt had been when he boarded a steam ship and left Ireland. He had quick Irish eyes and a desire to please Matt's daughter.

Today his eyes were dull. There was none of the usual teasing and chivalry. Instead, when he reached down to the half-empty glass of brandy on the table, his youthful hand trembled.

"William, you're tired."

"Four trips down."

"Helmet crew?"

164

"Yes. Middle of the night they put a call out for rescuers across the hill. Two of us came from the Poulin. We joined the Anaconda crews and went down."

"Must have been awful."

William nodded, "It was."

The men sat down across from each other while Linda directed the boys into the kitchen.

William continued, "We went to the 600, then the 700. They had just pulled up the first men. Smoke was so thick we had to feel our way, crawling, coming upon men lying in the tunnels. Checked for breathing but every last one of them was dead."

In the kitchen they could hear Linda ladling dinner onto their plates. Matt's youngest son came out, listening as William spoke, his eyes wide. He leaned against his father's side, his head on Matt's shoulder.

William tossed back the rest of his drink. "There can't be anybody alive down there," he said, staring at the empty glass. "Nobody can live in that."

"Did you see any signs of men still trapped?"

A somber look came over William's face. "We found some bodies together, naked, piled on top of each other."

Linda walked around the table placing dishes and asked quietly, "Why were they naked?"

"Looked like they tried to make a bulkhead. Close themselves in to keep the gas out. They wedged a door in a tunnel and nailed every stitch of clothing onto it, stuffed their pants and jumpers around the edges. But it didn't work, their room wasn't air tight. The gas came down behind them through a stope partly filled with waste rock. We found all of them huddled together by the bulkhead, maybe just to touch somebody at the end."

Linda turned away, holding a dish towel to her mouth.

Matt broke the silence, "Come now, let's be thankful for dinner." He gestured for the boys and Linda to sit down and folded his hands on the table in front of him and said a brief Grace.

"Holy Father, we pray for the families and their men. If any miners are still living, please bring them back to safety."

They ate in quiet. Linda glanced at her father, who sat with a somber expression, absorbed in thought. After several minutes, Matt abruptly pushed back his chair and stood, leaving most of his dinner untouched.

"I must excuse myself."

He walked around the table with a little smile for his boys, and put his hand on William's shoulder. The younger man looked up. "William," he said softly, "You should get some sleep before your next shift."

As Matt closed the door and stepped down onto the sidewalk, the June sun was setting, a yellow orb above the ridge of Big Butte Mountain at the western edge of the city. Its last rays slanted through tossed, broken clouds and splayed pale shadows onto the walkway. In front of him, horses tossed their heads, drivers called out and flicked reins in a stream of cabs, wagons, and puttering automobiles that bounced along on the cobblestone street.

Behind him, his neighbor Joe Barnicoat came out of his house and headed back to the turmoil at the Speculator after a few hours sleep.

Canning heard the footsteps and turned, "Evening, Joe."

Barnicoat looked up, "Matt."

"It's bad, isn't it?" asked Canning.

Barnicoat halted, strain heavy on his face. "I was at the mine all night and most of today. We're doing everything we can. I thought hell was for the hereafter, but there's no other word for it."

"I tried to find a couple of friends, they're missing."

"Who?"

"Thomas Carson, and Jigger Trelawney."

"Trelawney? Damn! Saw him head down with the shift Friday evening."

"Didn't find him or Carson on the identified lists earlier today."

Barnicoat shook his head, "Nobody knows for sure who's up or down. Men came up every which-where, the Corra, High Ore, Diamond. I seen a lot of faces."

166

"They were my partners. Kept me safe when I first went underground."

"Good working men, all of them," said Barnicoat. "And now this...."

"It seemed like everything was going well up there."

"We were ready for fire. Braly had two rail trucks on the surface set to go down, soda acid extinguishers, just had to roll them into a cage. But nobody thought we'd ever lose the hoist."

Matt listened carefully, then asked, "How did it start?"

"Big cable fell down the shaft. It was all ripped to pieces, and Sullau went below to pull it out. Got his lamp too close and the whole thing took fire."

Matt looked again at the rising smoke and Barnicoat followed his gaze.

"Smoke went so quick into the workings, miners on the sill couldn't get away. You wouldn't believe all the tags left on the 'in' board. We tried to prevent fire, but we walked right into it."

"What do you mean?"

"The cable was to power the sprinklers, to put fires out. But it started the fire. Don't know if that makes sense, but it's true."

Barnicoat took his watch out, "I got to get back, we're looking for survivors. Braly thinks that there may still be men alive in the north country."

"God be with you, Joe," said Matt, and his friend swung up into a moving trolley headed toward the eastside hill.

Matt hurried across Missoula Gulch. The wind blew him up the steep street, chasing knots of people through Uptown. He pulled his coat tight and tucked his chin, walking quickly along. Brick high rises lined either side of the street and trolleys moved past with a deep heavy roll and ringing bells. When he reached Main, he turned left directly up the hill toward the *Standard* office and scanned the hill above him, watching the iron-gray edges of smoke rise into the eastern sky.

A block up the street, a hushed crowd had gathered in front of the newspaper's doorway. People came from every direction as word spread that the mine had sent an updated list, giving the names of identified dead and survivors who had reached the surface alive. It had been hours since the last one was posted, but for those waiting it seemed much longer.

Matt came to the front of the *Standard* building and joined a crowd filling the sidewalk. An office worker opened the door and yelled out, "Got a new list right here!" People surged forward as he placed it in the window.

Matt was too far back to read the list and waited for a chance to check for his friends' names.

A newspaper boy selling the *Extra Evening Edition* pushed through the adults until he stood next to Matt. He had a satchel of papers slung over his shoulder and was six or seven years old, barely to Matt's waist, sizing people up with a street kid's determined eyes.

The cold breeze whirled a few scattered snowflakes from dark clouds, gusting around the edges of the buildings and spinning across the streets. The boy stood cap in hand, peering up at the list, and swiped his hair back from his forehead. Flakes stuck in his tousled mop for a few moments, then melted and dripped down his face.

The crowd stood close to the window, leaning over the top of the small boy as they read and looked for sons, relatives, and friends, hoping they would not find a familiar name. In the confusion, nobody quite knew who was alive and who might be missing.

The boy pulled anxiously on Canning's coat. "Hey, Mister, I can't see that list. Someone told me my daddy's there. Will you tell me?"

"What is your father's name?"

"It's Yebras, mister. My Pa's named Nick Yebras."

Matt ran his finger down the list of men missing. There, fourth down in the second column, was the father's name. He looked down into the boy's anxious face staring up at him. *He must be the same age as my little Matthew*, he thought.

Taking a deep breath, Canning said, "Son, your daddy is on the missing list. He's still underground. I'm sorry."

The boy stared at Matt and fingered his cap, his lips twitched. Matt put his hand on the boy's head.

"But I hope they find him today and he comes home."

The boy nodded. He wrapped his arm around the canvas satchel of papers that hung at his side and turned into the crowd, shouldering his way out.

"Extra! Extra!" he called out. "Lots of men killed in the mine!" He swaggered into the crowd yelling, "Anybody want the *Extra?*"

A man on the outskirts reached into his pocket for a nickel and yelled "Hey, kid! Right here!" and held it out, but the boy had stopped and didn't hear. Instead, he turned and looked back at the list in the window and stood swaying slightly as the realization dawned. His eyes widened, and he wiped a dirty hand across his face, his mouth working with emotion. The sling for the satchel slipped off his shoulder and his papers dropped to the pavement. He mouthed the word, "Pa..."

Matt pushed out of the crowd to say something to the boy, to help him. He picked up the fallen papers and put them back in the satchel, but the boy bolted away, leaving Matt with the satchel and the other man holding his nickel.

The boy's small back disappeared at a run up Main Street, dodging the trolleys and wagons, darting through the crowds of workers, and Matt heard his high-pitched voice through the noise of the traffic, "*Pa! Pa!*"

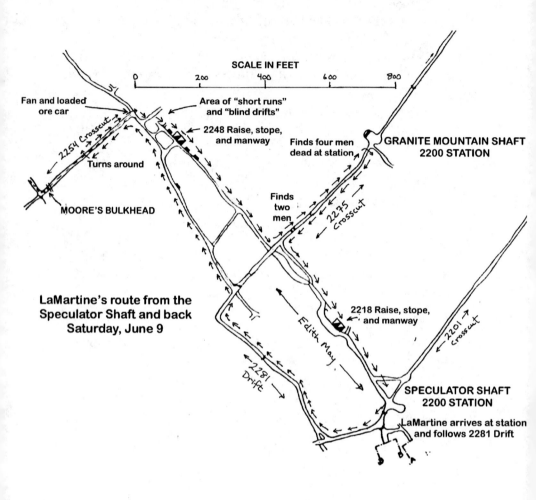

SCALE IN FEET

Fan and loaded ore car

Area of "short runs" and "blind drifts"

2254 Crosscut

2248 Raise, stope, and manway

Turns around

Finds four men dead at station

GRANITE MOUNTAIN SHAFT
2200 STATION

MOORE'S BULKHEAD

Finds two men

2275 Crosscut

LaMartine's route from the
Speculator Shaft and back
Saturday, June 9

2218 Raise, stope, and manway

Edith May

2281 Drift

2201 Crosscut

SPECULATOR SHAFT
2200 STATION

LaMartine arrives at station
and follows 2281 Drift

LaMartine's route exploring the 2200 level on Saturday,
June 9, 1917, starting from the Speculator station.

170

CHAPTER TWENTY-TWO

NINE BELLS ON THE 2200

At noon on Saturday, Tom LaMartine stood in the Speculator yard and heard the bells ring nine times for *danger*, then six and two for the 2200. Another rescuer yelled to him, "Tom! Can you go down?"

LaMartine had been a miner for twenty years, working first in the Speculator as a pipeman, then in the Leonard mine as head of safety. He was known for his careful logic and was one of the first men called when a mine needed help.

LaMartine had been to the 1800 level three times that morning with shift bosses Hamill and Goodell. They had entered through the Spec shaft and the High Ore, hauling dead men up into daylight. They all knew it was a race against time in the maze below, filled with steam, smoke, and gas.

He quickly slipped the straps of his breathing apparatus over his shoulders. The tubes and mouthpiece fell forward against his chest as he arranged the weight, adjusting the valves of his CO_2 scrubber. Twice that morning he had been forced to turn around because of malfunctions. In the drifts, any such problem could kill him.

"Careful," said the cage tender. LaMartine nodded, and they dropped down the shaft. Balancing in the cage, he snugged his nose clip on and stepped off at the 22 station. The air was smoky but breathable.

Out on the turnsheets, four men stood without helmets. After the constant threat of gas throughout the morning, LaMartine was surprised to see them without breathing gear on, but they quickly explained, "We come in from the Rainbow, following the good air, looking for men. Gas is clear from the main passages, but two of our boys, they gone ahead and is missing."

"Where'd they go?" asked LaMartine.

"That way," the man pointed to the tunnel to the left.

171

"They's got helmets," he added.

"How long?"

"Ten minutes."

"I'm on it."

This close to the shaft, the air was clear and his lamp flame was strong. Even so, he opened his oxygen valve and put in his mouthpiece to be safe, any tunnel could hide a fatal pocket of gas. He headed west, turning at the first switch into the Edith May workings.

I should run into them if I circle the west side, he thought. *Go out the 2281, then come back toward the Speculator on the main 2202.*

There were many secondary tunnels splitting off, and he quickly looked into each, moving along until he reached a four-way switch with the big 2275 crosscut coming from the Granite Mountain shaft. It was like a main street and he turned into it. Within a hundred feet, a wide haulage-way turned left to the northwest. He followed it, and just inside the tunnel there were three bodies face down, covered in ash. He stopped and involuntarily made the sign of the cross. *Looks like they were running to the shaft,* he thought, making a note of where they were, and said quietly, "We'll be back to get you."

Small crosscuts split off, little runs and blind drifts, which only went a short distance back. He walked a few feet into each one and found raises being cut up to the next level, showing that the stoping had just started. There were several drills, their bits half into the rock as if the crew had been stopped in the middle of a hole. Hoses, wheelbarrows, and shovels were strewn about. *Those three men likely had been working here when the smoke hit and ran for the station.*

A bit farther there was a wide crosscut to the left with rail tracks going in. A loaded ore car sat there and behind it, next to the wall, was a new electric fan with canvas piping attached that fed into the crosscut. Lagging boards had fallen from a stack near the fan, across the rails and up against the ore car. A canvas sack of nails lay there, ripped down one side, with nails spilled across the ground.

172

The crosscut headed west off the main drift, and was much wider than usual, almost ten feet across. *A lot of work going on there, maybe a lot of men,* he thought and cringed a little at the idea of a big group of bodies. *Should be checked.* He looked at the fan and the long electrical wire strung along the upper timbers; he had never seen an area so far from a shaft being ventilated.

The ore car was new, hardly dented. Muckers had filled it at the face back in the crosscut with good looking ore. *Waiting for the motor to pick it up. They wheeled it to the switch, so there must be a motor around here somewhere.*

His nerves tingled as he stepped inside the crosscut, slowly, watching his lamp flame. He slipped off his goggles to look for foot prints and could see the floor had been ruffled by gas moving over it. The humid air around him glistened slightly, as if he were looking through transparent gauze. He pulled a candle out and lit it. From long experience, he knew its flame was more sensitive than the carbide lamp. Every splutter and subtle change in brightness or color told him about the air.

Holding it at his waist the flame flickered and fell, then when raised to eye level, it grew. Carefully, he began a slow choreographed movement down the gassy crosscut, raising the candle up then down, back and forth, as if performing some arcane ritual, crossing himself as he moved ahead a few feet at a time.

After all the short runs and shallow dead-end drifts, he expected to reach the end of this crosscut quickly, but it kept going. There were signs of men, a compressed air line and a water pipe ran along the floor. Several hundred feet in, he felt his own tension mounting. *Be cautious*, he told himself, *you have no backup.*

Suddenly as he lowered his candle, it snuffed out, leaving him in darkness. He stood still with the hollow rasp of oxygen in his breathing tubes, and told himself, *Stay calm, breathe steadily.* The darkness was absolute and his balance wavered as he spun the starter of his lamp. Sparks flew, but it would not light.

He realized that in the stillness of the tunnel, the gas had stratified and he stood in a pool of carbon monoxide. His movements had stirred the gas as he came in, and it would be deadly all the way back to the entrance of the crosscut.

Sweat rolled down his forehead and dripped from his chin. Tapping his boot on the ground behind him, he felt for the edge of the rails, then slowly turned, and shuffled carefully back. He counted his short steps, judging where he was by touching the rails with his left foot, shuffling further, and tried his lamp several times.

Long minutes later, it finally took and burned weakly. The flame flared when he raised it over his head, pushing the darkness back and revealing the tunnel again. Holding the lamp high, he walked with an even, slow gait to the entrance, acutely aware of the hiss of his oxygen. With relief he stepped into the main drift where the lamp burned brightly.

He rested at the entrance and looked over the scene. A plank was nailed to the timber set above the opening with "2254" painted on it, the number of the crosscut. Checking the floor closely again, he could see there were no fresh boot tracks except his. Nobody had been in the tunnel since the fire. He had crossed all the main tunnels and still not found any trace of the two missing men he had been sent to find. *Well, they sure aren't in there*, he thought. *I hope they're okay.*

He turned southward, circling back toward the distant shaft. In a hundred feet, a new drift split to the left, paralleling the one he had come in on. *This must be the 2202*, he thought, the main drift along the Edith May vein. He took it, quickly reaching the intersection with the main 2275 crosscut that went to the Granite Mountain Station. As he turned into the 2275, he ran into the two men he was trying to find. They had stopped in the crosscut, looking at the bodies of two fallen miners laying with their arms outstretched, cut down by gas running toward the shaft.

"Hey," called LaMartine, "You boys okay?"

One of them pulled out his mouthpiece, "Yes, what are you doing here?"

"Your friends back at the station thought you'd gotten mixed up with the gas. They called up nine bells and sent me looking."

"Oh damn, sorry. We're heading back now."

"Have you run into gas?"

174

"Nothing too bad, lamps a little low."

LaMartine asked him, "How many got out of this area?"

"Don't know, but from the looks of the drifts, lots of men was working here." He put his hand on LaMartine's shoulder, "Thanks for looking for us."

"Tell the cage tender I'll be back shortly."

The men left for the Spec. LaMartine passed the bodies and went down the tunnel toward the Granite Mountain station, thinking, *With all the signs of work, there should be more men.*

In a few minutes, the station lay in front of him echoing with the sound of running water. The station was an ugly heap of rock shards and slabs, and the timber sets had burned fifty feet back from the station's opening to the entrance of the crosscut. Nothing was left but a hollowed smoking wreck. Water coursed down, smattering and splashing on the edge of the shaft, dripping past the station as smoke swirled upward in a breeze. The smell of wet burned timber and smoldering came through his nose clip. Near the shaft the metal turnsheets had buckled into V-shapes from the heat of the fire and were partly buried under rubble.

On the other side of the station, legs and torsos caught his eye, sticking out of the rock debris. He peered closely, looking for any movement, took his mouthpiece out and called, "Hey! Anybody here?" There was no response. There was no way he could get the buried bodies by himself, so he returned to the Speculator station.

When he reached the surface he talked with Rosie Smith and Superintendent Frink, and reported what he had found. "The 22 looks like it had lots of men working, little runs and blind drifts, drills and fresh stoping. But only a few bodies. We need to check that area more. How many men got out?"

Next he went down with the Tramway team investigating the 1800 and 2000 in the Edith May workings. The ventilation doors near the Granite Mountain station were so hot they could not be touched. They found bodies along the drifts and pulled them out in canvas sheets. Surfacing after fourteen hours and five trips into the workings, he checked into the Speculator office. Boardman, the head of the safety teams sent him home.

"You're a wreck, Tom. Get some sleep."

175

CHAPTER TWENTY-THREE

THE MAYOR AND THE CORONER

Along the streets, people stood by the morgues in hopeless resignation. Inside, men in worn work clothes and heavy boots walked softly, trying not to disturb others in their grief. Women draped in black sat by coffins, saying quiet prayers, as a constant stream of people came through and scenes of pathos were everywhere.

At the Speculator, bodies were raised and put in the mineyard at a temporary morgue. The mine gates were opened and a long line of men and women were allowed to pass between the benches to identify relatives or friends. Whenever one was identified it was transferred Uptown. Quickly, all of the city's undertakers were filled to capacity.

Next to the headframe, caskets were piled in stacks and bodies on collapsible stretchers. Thirty-five more victims were brought up that afternoon, but only one was recognized. People were frantic, unable to find their men, demanding answers.

Saturday after dark the mayor ordered the first seven unidentified bodies secretly taken away to the cemetery and buried. When the news of this broke out, there was an uprising of anger.

The next morning, Mayor Maloney and Coroner Lane faced off against each other at the Speculator mineyard, surrounded by a pressing crowd. The two men held onto decorum, but were red-faced and their voices clipped.

"There are too many men who can't be identified. It's only going to get worse," the mayor stated.

The coroner was adamant, "The bodies that can be exposed to public view, must be placed on the benches today so relatives can try to identify them. We owe that to the families."

"Most can't be handled. They have to be buried to protect public health," the mayor replied, "People are horrified looking at them. Mats of hair falling off. Their noses are buried between their bloated lips and cheeks. The faces are beyond recognition. We have to do something."

"The families have had their men's lives taken from them. Now you're going to take the bodies too! They'll never know where their fathers are, or where their husbands are. And the death records will be absolute chaos."

The argument escalated, voices sharpened.

"We are going to put them into mass graves in the Mountain View Cemetery," the mayor said flatly. "We had men digging all night in that damned rocky ground, but the caskets will be neat and organized in long rows."

The coroner became angry, "We don't know who is in single casket!"

"We buried seven bodies last night and there will be more. It's the only solution."

"You mean you goddamn stole seven bodies last night! Hid them in the ground without anybody knowing! No Christian burial! Can't you even summon a minister? People are asking, 'Where is God in all this?'" said the coroner, "You are denying Him!"

The mayor broke in, "All will be buried immediately. The police will enforce my order."

"You can't steal away our men!" The coroner pointed to the angry crowd around them, who were now grumbling angrily. "I am the authority here and ..."

"I'm calling the police," the mayor said to his aide. "We will remove the bodies to the cemetery."

"You can't ..." yelled the coroner.

"I can," he swept his hand and two officers came to his side.

The coroner balled up his fists and stepped up into the mayor's face, but a policeman put his hand between them. They stared at each other until the mayor said softly to the coroner, "Mr. Lane, God is in the courage and sacrifice of the rescuers and those helping. It's all we can do."

CHAPTER TWENTY-FOUR

TWO LADIES

Mrs. Tregonning leaned on the arm of the sofa with her legs folded beneath her. Tensely, she peered out the living room window for some sign of her husband coming down Colorado Street, then sank back down.

Her neighbor sat in a chair next to her. Mrs. Trelawney's husband had also been working deep and was missing. She came over to the house to comfort the young mother, sitting there through the day, the rapid clicks of her knitting needles filling the silences in their conversation.

"My man's been a miner twenty years, and this ain't the first time he's been late," Mrs. Trelawney said to her friend. "I remember when a timber got him, broke his leg and I found him in the hospital. I asked how it happened, and he wouldn't answer. And I said, 'It's too dangerous down there', and he brushed it off, 'Timber could of fallen on my head,' he said, 'but it didn't'."

Mrs. Trelawney dropped her knitting into her lap. "When he got better, I said, 'You could get a job on the surface, maybe topman.' But he told me, 'I work rock and I always will'."

She patted her young friend's arm, "You can't tell these men anything."

Long minutes went by, and Mrs. Tregonning pressed her temples with her fingertips, her eyes shut tight.

"Ben knew the mine so well he would never get lost. And he is too capable a miner to get caught down there," the younger woman said. "If any man had a fighting chance, it would be him. I know this in my heart."

The neighborhood outside was nearly empty, the usual busyness had disappeared and quiet sifted into the house.

"He was rocking way below the fire, but the rescue teams haven't gotten that far yet. Someone said they heard noises, tapping on the pipes. Maybe the men are waiting it out. The gas, you know," she said, gesturing weakly with her hand.

178

"Miners know where to go to stay safe," comforted Mrs. Trelawney.

Mrs. Tregonning glanced around the room. "I have been so frightened. If the telephone rings I can't bear to answer it. I think somebody will tell me my Ben is dead..."

"Rescuers are at the mine, going down to help," said Mrs. Trelawney. "They'll find our men."

"I would never have the courage to go underground," said Mrs. Tregonning, "but Ben spent years down there. I know he would save anyone he could."

"People know that," said Mrs. Trelawney. "He is a good man."

Their voices trailed off, each left in her own thoughts. Worn hands moved again with short strokes and loops. Mrs. Trelawney blinked back tears and her practiced hands dropped a stitch. Reflexively, she pinched just below to stop the yarn from unraveling. When she started again, her needles trembled.

Mrs. Tregonning broke the quiet. "Yesterday, Ben said he would tell Foreman Sullau he was going to take work as a salesman again. I asked him to, I didn't want him to get hurt." Short shuddering breaths caught in her throat.

Mrs. Trelawney stuck her knitting needles into the ball of yarn and leaned forward, taking the young woman's hand and holding it gently. "If I had no hope, I would be miserable. You must have hope."

Mrs. Tregonning did not reply. Her friend's eyes sought her gaze, but she stared into the empty street.

The doorway to the children's room opened and two little heads poked out. "Mama?" they called. She held out her arms and the boys came running to her, climbed into her lap, and she held them close.

CHAPTER TWENTY-FIVE

MEN ALIVE ON THE 2400

Twenty-nine men labored to fill their lungs in the heat-thickened darkness. They had spent nearly two days behind the bulkhead. It was impossible to find comfort, and all were struggling.

Through the endless hours, their thoughts blurred and their eyes strained for a glimmer of light. Shea and Wirta lay sluggishly on the floor while Duggan spun the self-lighter on his lantern with his thumb. The flint kicked small quick sparks, thin streaks arcing across his vision.

Duggan reached over and pulled the shirt out, then shook Wirta's shoulder, "John, smell this." In a daze, Wirta sniffed the cloth and Duggan added, "It's clearing outside."

"Clearing?"

Duggan whispered, "Now's the time."

Wirta sat up, "I'm with you."

They worked by touch, felt for the board at the top of the bulkhead and pried it loose with a crow bar. The noise woke the men behind them. "What you doing?" came a voice.

"Breaking it down."

"What?"

"Air outside is clearing," said Duggan. "You boys ready to take the gambler's chance?"

"Hell yes," said Fowler.

Duggan and Wirta were joined by Johnson and Shea. They tore the canvas frame down, nails screeching, then pitched into the thick mud-caked bulkhead, with sand and dirt flying. Duggan took a shovel and broke the next board with a sharp crack, then pried it off. A wash of cool air from outside flowed over them.

"My God," said Wirta, taking a deep breath, "Air."

"What's going on?" said Stewart.

180

Duggan called over his shoulder, "We're getting out," and broke a second board free, then another. Within a few minutes the bulkhead was down.

The new air flooded in and woke the rest. It had come from the June morning far above, from a world with a sun, a world with light, pushed by the fans at the Gem and Rainbow and from the Speculator, thousands of feet through the shafts and into the workings. The men could smell life, they were hungry for it, and hope rose in them.

Duggan pulled himself over the broken boards and stood weakly outside. Then he began staggering away into the darkness. A few more crawled over the wreckage of the bulkhead that had saved them, and stopped outside to rest from the effort. Then slowly, like blind men, in ones and twos they started making their way unsteadily out of the long dead-end crosscut.

Duggan was far in the lead. He stumbled and fell once, then he gathered himself on all fours, climbed to his feet and continued. Out of the dead-end he went, pushing himself, turning into the long 2401 crosscut toward the Speculator station. Ten years in this mine, he knew the way by heart even now.

He concentrated on each step, staying upright and feeling stronger. Finally, he reached the station and dropped down to crawl closer to the open shaft. There was one thing he had to know: *Were the bells in?* If they had fixed the shaft and were hoisting from this level, the signal bells would be there. He searched for the pull cord, quickly running his hands back and forth across the timber framing the outside of the shaft, but found nothing. The steel housing was there, but no cord.

It's like I thought. They didn't finish retimbering. No cages coming down here. He turned around and began to retrace his steps away from the station. He heard scraping feet coming toward him in the darkness and he called out, "It's Duggan, who's there?"

"McAdams," came a raspy voice.

"There isn't any signal cord," Duggan said. "The shaft isn't fixed. Come with me to the Rainbow. We'll get a rescue team for the rest." McAdams turned and followed Duggan back up the 2401

181

crosscut, they passed the opening to the dead-end where they had bulkheaded, and continued into the north country.

Back in the dead-end crosscut, most of the men were still near the bulkhead, or had not yet climbed over. Wirta lay on the floor just outside, breathing deeply. The air was cooler and fresher, but had a trace of gas left from the days before. He pulled himself to his feet and walked unsteadily, feeling his way along. His mind was muddled, but when the drift opened up, he knew he had reached the main crosscut. He had never been hoisted through the Spec shaft and only knew the general direction. *It's south*, he thought, and turned right, unsure of how far he had to go.

Shea stood leaning on the broken bulkhead, encouraging the men, "There's good air now. We'll make it." Fowler and Negretto rose, and then others, until there was a ragged line of stragglers in the pitch black, all of them fixed on reaching the Speculator station, unaware that Duggan was already heading away from them farther out the 2401 toward the Rainbow.

Wirta passed the switch into the Jessie stopes, then the switch leading to the Granite Mountain, stragglers came behind him. Finally, he could feel a fresh draft of air on his face, coming from the Old Spec.

He reached the station first, and sensed the hollow distance before him. Cautiously, he bent down and got on all fours, crawling across the steel turnsheets. Gritty ore shards jabbed into his palms and knees and every arm length he reached out, brushing his hand over the sheet in front of him before he moved forward again. He did not know the layout of the station, but a dozen or more feet ahead was the edge of the shaft itself, and a fall meant death.

Tapping, reaching, he found the shaft's edge, put both hands on the timber frame and slowly inched upright, feeling up and down the timbers on either side of the shaft for the signal bells. His hands passed over the steel housing, but it was empty. There was no pull cord.

"Where's the damn bells?" he muttered.

Frustrated, he brushed his hands over the timbers again, slower this time.

"They got to be here..."

182

He tried to think clearly, but carbon monoxide lingered inside him in a dulling fog and his attention swayed. Standing right on the edge of the shaft, even in the darkness he could feel the chasm before him, a visceral sense of emptiness, little echoes that fell away below.

He heard scraping sounds behind him, as several more men made it to the turnsheets. 'Hey," he said. "It's Wirta, who's there?"

"Johnson and Shea," came the answers from twenty feet away. "You at the shaft?"

"Yeah, but I can't ring the hoist. Ain't no bell cord."

There was more shuffling and scraping, then the two men joined him. Johnson carefully stood upright and felt around the timbers, "Nothing here but the housing."

"What should we do, find a manway?"

They were quiet a few moments, thinking. "Try in the shaft," said Johnson. "The pull cord might be hanging there, if they ain't strung it to the box yet."

"Could be," Wirta paused, "Hold onto my arm." Johnson and Shea braced themselves, gripping the edge of the timber frame with one hand, grasping Wirta's grimy hand and wrist with the other.

Wirta said, "Don't let go," and leaned slowly into the open shaft. His heart rushed from his chest, and a hundred voices inside him screamed. He fought to control himself, feeling along the timbers inside, passing his hands across the teak guides on the wall, smoothed by cages passing thousands of times. Nothing. He carefully stretched out, swung his arm across, and something brushed the back of his hand, light and moving. *What was that?*

"Hold tight, I'm leaning farther." The men tightened their grips and he reached into the empty void. Slowly his hand swung, feeling the darkness. One swing, then another. On the third his hand hit a cord gently waving in the down-welling air. It bounced out of his palm, but he swung again and it caught on his fingers.

"Caught it," he said, grasping the cord, and they pulled him back. "It's coming from the pull bottle on the level above, but ain't attached here yet."

"Do it work?"

183

"Give it a try."

With the other men still holding onto him, Wirta pulled the cord and could feel the little hitch in the tension and a buzz, "She's sounding. Hope somebody hears."

He rang the signal for danger, nine bells straight, counting carefully one by one. Then the level, *six bells,* pause, *four.*

He started again, pulling slowly and counting out loud, "one, two, three..."

Above, at the hoist room for the Speculator, the engineer sat at the control levers and lit the cigarette he had just rolled. He let out a long breath and tapped the ashes off on the railing around his chair, waiting for another signal from the rescue teams on the 1800 and 2000. They had been lifting and lowering rescuers between the 600 and 2200 all day.

The hoist bells rang and he looked over at them, reflexively counting the rings, *... seven, eight, nine.* Nine bells, *danger.* He sat up and said to himself, "Where are they ringing from?"

He stared at the bells and they rang again, hesitantly, *six bells,* pause, *four bells,* for the 2400 level. Then again, nine slow, deliberate bells for *danger.*

"There ain't no rescuers there...," he said aloud.

The rings repeated, and he listened, alert and trembling. *Six bells,* pause, *four bells.*

"Call the men at the shaft collar!" he yelled to a man standing by the door. "We got men on the 2400! Send a cage down!" The shaft collar exploded in a rush of activity as the news spread. Rescuers quickly grabbed helmets and the rattling cage descended.

Below the men waited in the dark and finally heard the creak of the cables moving. "They're coming," said Shea, and he broke down and sobbed with relief, "My God, we're saved."

Light appeared in the shaft as the cage lowered into view. The bars of the cage shot open, and rescuers stepped into the station with lanterns splaying light.

Several more men had made it to the station from the bulkhead and were sitting on the turnsheets. Light from the rescuers' lanterns spread over the station and eight mostly naked

184

men looked back at them, covered with scrapes and smeared with dirt, faces hollow and exhausted. They blinked painfully at the first light in days.

A bare-headed doctor immediately bent over Wirta, who had slumped over next to the shaft. He checked for a pulse, then looked at the others. "Thank God, you're alive."

***

Word spread fast and a crowd gathered around the headframe, men cheering and joyous as lost miners stepped out of the cage. Wirta, Johnson, and Negretto came first, Wirta slumped into the arms of the helmet men and had to be helped to the Speculator office, then to the hospital. The cage returned underground to bring up another load of weakened men.

An ever larger crowd peered through the mineyard's fence as the miners continued to come up, the people unable to believe that there were so many men alive after nothing but deaths. They burst into tears of relief, shouting and hugging.

Bodnaruk leaped out of the cage and ran into a crowd of his Croatian friends, kissing them on the cheek and slapping their backs to the crowd's unbridled happiness. Somebody asked him whether he would ever mine again, "Sure!" he laughed, "I'm going back to work the mines, and the Speculator if I get the chance!" He drank from a whiskey bottle that somebody stuck in his hand and toasted the cheering crowd. "A man has only one time to die and it may as well be underground as on top. It's all in the game."

Most of the miners were naked and given coats that they pulled over their scraped and filthy bare backs. First aid workers draped Fowler and LaMontague with blankets and the two men stood for a photographer. LaMontague wrote a quick telegram for his fiancée in Missoula, "I'm alive. The wedding is still on!" Spihr stuffed himself with sandwiches. Other men were treated by the doctors, coffee put in their hands and food to eat.

The word spread quickly all over the city by the joy of the crowds, "Did you hear about the miracle? Twenty-five men alive!"

It took some time before people realized that Duggan had

not come to the surface and that nobody knew where he was. The men remembered contradictory things, some swore they had seen him at the station, others said he may have been delirious. He was hitting the pipes they said, he was talking incoherently about getting water for the men. Another asserted he had somehow seen Duggan back at the bulkhead, staggering. Albert Cobb and the others spoke with Budelier who already had his gear on, "He's gone toward the Rainbow is my guess." Rescue teams were quickly put together and sent to check the possible routes he might have taken.

The news of his disappearance, so close to being saved, put a sudden damper on the happiness, "He saved us all, none of us would have escaped alive if it hadn't been for him," said Shea. "I pray he is alive."

***

Cobb joked on the outside but was overwhelmed with relief, and desperate to see his wife. He peeled himself away from the first aid and the celebrating crowd and set off over the ridge, cut past the Diamond and down through Centerville, walking as fast as he could along the tracks that split the Gray Rock and Wake Up Jim, against the ten-foot high wooden fence for the Mountain Con's mineyard.

He made it to the upper blocks of Wyoming Street and reached the tiny yard, still reeking from the bulkhead. Their dog started barking, its hair standing on end as if he didn't recognize Cobb. He spoke to it, commanded it, but the dog wouldn't let him come in the yard.

His wife burst out of the house, yelling "Albert!" and the neighbors stepped into the street. Still the dog would not let him pass. She tore into the house in a frenzy and grabbed a shirt and pair of his pants, throwing them over the fence. He shed his filthy clothes and put the new ones on, shirt inside out, and opened the gate, the dog leaped for joy and his wife flung herself on him.

"I knew it would end like this," she said. "I never quit."

CHAPTER TWENTY-SIX

Aching for Light

Blackness filled the air like a substance, infusing blindness into their eyes, stealing their vision of shapes and their companions. It seeped into their legs and hands, into their ears and thoughts. The hope and expectancy that filled them after they had built the bulkhead weakened, giving way to a tinge of desperation.

Moore roused himself from the haze of the poisoned air to talk with the men, to rap on the pipe, and keep hope alive for when rescuers came. He crawled with the small wooden keg of water, only a few inches sloshing in the bottom, tipping it up to get a dollop into the men's mouths and on their lips. Some refused because it was too difficult to sit up and drink, still, he softly encouraged them.

Lisa and Marthey joined Moore, felt for each man's head and propped it up. Marthey held the men from the back, and they found the edge of his mouth and poured a sip of water in. Men murmured and accepted the offering. Truax was too weak to take a drink. Erikson croaked a few syllables, saying, "Yes, water."

One man became agitated when he woke. He understood little English and Friday night had been his first shift in the mine. Terrified, he was breaking down and had not accepted any water for the last twenty-four hours.

In the dark, he crawled on hands and knees over the others, up to the bulkhead. Moore heard him coming, shuffling and scraping. "Where you going?" Moore asked.

"Out," came a thick accent in a dry throat. "Me, out."

"You ain't going nowhere. Sit back down."

The man grabbed at Moore, fumbling and desperate. "Must … out," he said again, half pleading, half demanding.

Moore knew only a strong hand would stop the desperation. He barked in a clipped tone, "If you break it, you'll die like a rat. Now, get down." Lisa and Marthey stayed close, surrounding him.

Lisa spoke next, "We can't go out until the air clears."

There was a long silence, then Moore patted the man on the shoulder and said gently, "We'll make it, but you got to wait."

The man wavered, then crawled back and lay down in the mud.

Moore listened carefully to the movements until he was satisfied the man was not going to rush them, then he let himself relax, his arms and body burning from the effort. He lay down against the bulkhead panting lightly, with Sullivan and Lisa to his side. Each fell back into his own suffering, their bodies scattered about in the darkness.

In the chamber, the stench tasted thick and fetid like a sewer. The air had been breathed and rebreathed, sucked of its oxygen. Like a body starving on thin gruel, their throats and lungs opened, expecting the sustenance of air, but nothing filled the emptiness.

Their eyes ached for light, to see anything that might tell them they were human and alive, groaning in agony. Inside each of them the fine architecture of life, the heart itself, began to misfire and weaken, and slowly started to fail.

CHAPTER TWENTY-SEVEN

LaMartine into the 2254

At four o'clock on Sunday morning, LaMartine opened his eyes with a half-hollow feeling like he had never been asleep. He had spent the night sweating through fragmented dreams, urgently searching dark tunnels and blind corners. Now sitting up in a gritty bed, questions from the day before crowded into his mind.

Where were the men from the 22? He had only found five, and he knew there were sixty or more men working on the Edith May stopes. Moore himself, the shifter, was missing.

The messy area next to the loaded ore car bothered him too. Everywhere signs of work, but no men...

If we can find the motor, there should be drillers and other men close by, maybe a whole stoping crew, he thought, *There's no way out of that back area except to the Granite Mountain shaft, so where did they go?*

Cold logic in the early morning. Four cups of coffee and at the Spec two hours early, he was ready to go down.

The time keeper O'Keefe saw him and spoke, "Hey Tom, it's not even five."

"Couldn't sleep."

"I know the feeling," said O'Keefe, clocking in LaMartine. "There are over a hundred men still unaccounted for."

"More than a hundred?"

The timekeeper pointed at the tags on the "in" board. They exchanged a wordless look. "Careful down there, Tom."

LaMartine gave a small wave and walked out.

In the dries, LaMartine overheard the Speculator shaftmen who had just come up off the chippy hoist.

"Almost finished. Set the last two timbers. They're hanging signal bells below the 2000," one said, "Maybe we can get to the 2400 today."

Only one reconnaissance team had been down to the 24 on Saturday. At midafternoon, Budelier had taken a helmet crew

189

through the High Ore, reporting terrible conditions, brutal steam and smoke, and no sign of living men. With that grim knowledge, Manager Braly had focused searches on the levels above the fire.

He spoke to the helmet men going off shift, his face haggard after working thirty hours straight. He had reached the mine at midnight Saturday, sent an initial telegram to the main office in New York, and fought the chaos ever since. New York had sent constant requests for updates, but Braly told Frink to answer them while he focused on the miners. Throughout Saturday he directed rescue, sought to put the fire out and clear gas from the workings. He was a hands-on miner, and multiple times went underground with helmet teams to see for himself what was going on, and to help any way he could. Even though they were exhausted, the men listened carefully to him.

"Boardman and I have set a schedule through the drifts. We've searched to the 1800, and today we'll get into the 2000 and 2200, maybe lower. It's too dangerous to stretch the teams across all the levels, but we have to push. If there are live men down there, we have to find them right away."

Below 3200 feet, the mine tunnels were underwater. Shift boss Ben Tregonning was missing, as were many of the men working below the 2400. LaMartine winced at the thought of Tregonning, who had been his boss years ago. A man could never ask for a cooler or sharper head underground. Everybody on the rescue teams was painfully aware that other shift bosses, JD Moore and George Gorrie, were missing too.

"There's still gas in a lot of places. We're putting in brattices on the 1800 through 2200 to control the drafts and pull it out. Six went in last night and this morning," said Braly. "If you come across brattices, don't disturb them. They're holding the air course through the workings and up the shaft. We hope to clear the gas enough that you can start using the smaller thirty-minute tanks and get into the stopes, where we expect to find more men."

He held up his hand for the men's attention, "And don't take chances. There is enough death without yours."

After Braly left, the banter swirled. Men talked about who was alive, who had been identified. Across the yard, the warehouse was filled, the coroner and mayor had almost gotten in a fist fight arguing about health hazards and proper burial.

What would happen to the eight horses that had died down on different levels? Several had bolted and run with the ore cars behind, crashing and falling, and derailed cars blocked the crosscuts. For their protection, all rescue men were ordered to use camphor nose sheets. Time was getting by them and conditions were worsening.

The waves of comments washed around LaMartine. He listened, but said nothing.

The Tramway crew came early, with the same absorbed look on their faces as LaMartine. He had all his gear on, his goggles pulled back on his domed forehead, and his short curly brown hair stuck out from under his cap. He sat waiting on a bare wooden bench, tight lipped and ready. The leader, Rosie Smith, a compact, intense man with broad shoulders, entered the room and looked over at LaMartine, raising his eyebrows in recognition.

Smith shook his hand, all business, "Tom, I've talked with Braly. We need your help. You know the run of the country west of the Spec?"

LaMartine nodded, "I was pipeman there, six years ago, and I was down there yesterday."

"Okay, guide us."

Lowering to the High Ore station on the 2200, LaMartine led Smith and the Tramway men into the west Speculator workings. Approaching from the south, they found a rail flat truck in a side drift. "Grab that," said LaMartine, "we'll need it to bring the bodies out." There were seven men in the group, and they followed LaMartine back into the 2275 crosscut leading to the Granite Mountain. He and Rosie conferred, and on LaMartine's insistence, they decided to get the bodies from the Granite station first, then go up the drift near the fan and get the others.

The men were able to work without using their breathing apparatus, although they could still smell smoke and enough gas that two of the rescuers became dizzy. LaMartine stood with Rosie looking into the blown-out station.

"Probably got here, thinking they'd be hoisted. But the gas

came," said LaMartine, "Then the fire."

Rosie answered, "I talked with some of the guys from this level, Finnlander named Voko, his partner Wynder. They said a wall of smoke come from the Granite, men was passing them, their own partners even. Man named Roberts crawled right over them to the station. He must be one of those we just picked up. Voko said, he and Wynder only made it because they turned around and got out to the High Ore."

LaMartine looked at the bodies wrapped and lying on the rail truck, "Gas must have come strong."

It was midafternoon when the group began the long haul from the Granite Mountain shaft back to the High Ore. They did not have time to get the five bodies LaMartine had found farther up the drift.

At the intersection of the main 2275 crosscut the group turned left into the 2202 tunnel, back toward the Speculator station and High Ore. LaMartine stopped and told Rosie, "I'm taking Rabs," pointing to one of the other men.

"Where?"

"Back that way," he gestured. "I was here yesterday, saw some things that need checking. I'd like to find where the motor is and if there might be men back there." He chose his words carefully. "Them at the station, I don't think they were the drilling crew. We got to find those men, for their families."

"By my watch you got maybe an hour," Smith waved him on, "give or take. Meet back at the High Ore, or on top."

"If the air's okay over there, we won't use our apparatus."

Smith left with his men and the rail truck.

"Come on," LaMartine motioned to Rabs, "Let's find that motor."

They walked all the way to the end of the main drift. The only foot prints were LaMartine's from the day before. Tiny particles of white ash were sprinkled evenly on the ground, making the drift a pale milky color. As soon as they scuffed it, underneath was a layer of black soot.

He checked the air, it was gassy and they started their oxygen and put in their mouthpieces. They walked past the short drifts and runs, past the fan and open crosscut with the single ore car. There were no bodies or any disturbances, and the drift kept going. They followed the rails and finally ran into the motor, hooked to a train of nine cars, fully loaded with ore. It had been deserted just as it was ready to pull the trip to the Granite Mountain.

LaMartine said to Rabs, "I think the bodies in the 2275 crosscut are probably the motorman and swamper." He looked up and down the tunnel trying to see what had happened, "They must have got the alarm, and run out. Seems like they would have been ahead of the men coming down from the stopes."

Something about it confused him. "But if the gas came so fast the motorman didn't have time to get out, how could anybody else make it out?" He walked carefully around the train of cars, "And he must of had a head start too, so I don't get it. Where are the other men? The drilling crews? The men up in the stopes?"

They started back along the drift and LaMartine asked Rabs, "What do you make of it?" as they looked into a manway. "They got caught in the stopes and couldn't make it down here to the sill, or ... what?" He peered up the dark ladder into the workings above them, shining his lamp in, frowning.

"Well, they'd still be up there," said Rabs. "We got a lot of searching to do."

They went back to the same crosscut LaMartine had been in the day before, the sign above it was marked "2254".

"I didn't go to the end," he said to Rabs, "Possible there's a drilling crew back there, if they couldn't get out."

The tunnel disappeared into the darkness before them. It was wide, probably going to be made into a main haulage line. He could see his tracks from the day before, but there were no signs of anyone else. The fallen stack of boards was partly over the tracks. A bag of nails had seemingly been dropped on the side and scattered across the ground.

"What you thinking?" asked Rabs.

LaMartine pulled out his mouthpiece, "Well, look at the mess. Something was going on here."

Rabs shrugged, "Maybe the men was running out. Or

193

maybe the boys stacking it wasn't careful."

LaMartine picked up a dusty broken piece of ore from the pile in the car, "Yeah, could be. I mean, we got a loaded car setting here, waiting for the motorman." He threw the piece of ore at the fan against the wall, it hit the metal panel with a clang and fell to the floor. "Then we got this fan here, pushing air into the cut." Gesturing down he said, "Air hose, water pipe going in. A stack of lagging boards here, I think they was going to make a trolley box. There should be a working vein back there, and maybe some bodies." He looked into the drift, "Let's go in farther."

They walked in and LaMartine went slowly, raising and lowering his lamp, then moving it side to side, checking for gas with a slow crossing movement. He was more cautious after the problem the day before. The air was crystal clear and seemed to shimmer as it got closer to the floor. LaMartine had seen drifts like this after a fire, humid gassy air settled toward the floor like morning dew, and the surface between the layers wavered. He lifted the lamp higher and it burned brighter. The tiny crystal faces across the granite walls winked in his light.

A reflection caught his attention. Above him, a wire stretched along the upper corner of the timber sets with small curved hangers dangling from it. He reached up and flicked one, "Canvas piping from the fan was taken down. Left these." He could see loose hangers dangling down every few feet.

The crosscut went on for a surprising distance through bare granite, straight and wide. Here and there along the way, they came across different objects, first a hammer in the middle of the tracks, and a lagging board laying half on the side of the ties. After four hundred feet they reached a brattice walling off the tunnel, made of one-inch lagging boards. They were all nailed tight, cleanly built, the boards upright instead of horizontal. To the side of the drift, a Leyner drill stood, while the air hose and water pipe on the floor went underneath the boards.

LaMartine looked carefully around the edges of the wooden brattice. The lagging had been nailed tightly together, with streaks of mud exuding out of the cracks and along the sides where it butted into the rock wall. He pressed on it with his hands and it did not give at all. *Is this one of the new ones Braly said not to disturb?*

Rabs broke the silence, "Tom, what we waiting for?"

"You know," LaMartine said, "as a rule we throw up a brattice from the side we're working on, and paste it with canvas. This looks like it was built from the other side."

He pondered another few moments. "Rabs, you think maybe there's another tunnel on the other side that connects back into the main drift? Could be they were trying to keep that separate. Maybe that's why they got the fan at the entrance."

"Don't know," said Rabs.

LaMartine tried to get a grip on one of the boards to tear it off. It was nailed tightly and he could not get his fingertips in the spaces. He looked around on the floor and found a short wedge broken off the end of a lagging board. At eye-level, he stuck the wedge into a hole between the boards and prodded around. It pushed against something soft and he felt the mud give way, but he could not make a hole.

***

Unconscious on the other side, neither Moore nor any of the other men heard the muffled noises of the rescuers. They had built the bulkhead with all their mining knowledge, determined to shut out the gas. They were too good miners, for they had shut out more than the gas.

When LaMartine poked the sharp wedge of lagging board into the hole, it pushed into the soft leather of Moore's boot, nailed onto the boards. A clot of half-dried mud crumbled loose and fell, landing next to Moore's outstretched hand, sleeping and unaware.

***

LaMartine pulled the wedge out. "Maybe the drill team blocked off this end of the crosscut and they are working on the other side," he said. "Didn't want to reroute the air or water, so they took it in under the brattice."

195

Rabs nodded and mumbled through his mouthpiece, "Looks like it was just put up. Could be it's one of Braly's new brattices." He eyed his watch, "Tom, we got twenty minutes to make it out."

They started to leave, but LaMartine stopped. He put his hands on the dusty wood, then hammered with a fist and took his mouthpiece out. He called out several times, "Hey! Hello!" but everything was quiet.

They headed back, picking up two of the bodies from the drift and pushing them in an ore car.

It was nearly five when they made it to the Spec station, and he checked in with the shift boss who was waiting for them. Two other men took the bodies off the car and put them into the cage. LaMartine took off his goggles and mouthpiece, face streaked with sweat and grime. "We were out in the workings west, far Edith May."

"Was just about to come looking for you," the boss said. "Rosie left word to keep an eye out, if you was late."

"We didn't find any tracks. Brought those bodies. There's more too. But, we found some things that should be checked."

"What's that?" the boss cocked an eyebrow at him.

"This brattice at the end of the crosscut farthest to the northeast. It's solid, and no doorway, just shut off. Might be for ventilation, but looks like it's thrown up from the blind side. And there's three other bodies back in the main drift. Tramway boys didn't get them. Somebody's got to go back with stretchers."

The man made some notes. "I'll pass that along."

Another ten minutes of walking through the south tunnels and they reached the High Ore station. The tender was excited, "You hear? Men found alive, on the Spec 24. They need more helmet men, you got to get down there. They're still rescuing them."

LaMartine and Rabs were lowered down the High Ore to the 2400, and went across to the Spec station, where they found a crowd of ten or more helmet men. The rescued men had already been hoisted. "Nobody's left here," said the crew leader, "But they need help on the 2800, somebody said they heard tapping on the rails. You know that country?"

196

"Yes," said LaMartine.

"Take the High Ore shaft down." Back they went to the High Ore and were lowered to the waiting team.

The 2800 level was the worst yet. Nearly one thousand feet of the Granite Mountain shaft had caved in above them, restricting the air flow in the lower levels. Dense smoke and gas had backed up and their lamps would not light. It was hard to believe that anyone could still be alive there. LaMartine led them along the tracks out to the closest raise west of the Speculator, the 2807, where he thought men may have tried to climb from the 28 to the 26.

They crawled along the rails feeling for direction, Rabs behind LaMartine, then the rest of the group, one at the feet of the other. Their breathing apparatus weighed them down, and with lips distended they sucked on the bitter rubber mouthpieces. No bodies or men were found.

It was eight in the evening when they made it back to the surface at the High Ore. McNeal, the foreman of the High Ore, was in better spirits when he saw LaMartine in the yard. "Tom, you heard about Duggan's men? Twenty-five men came out alive from the 2400. Thank God, a miracle."

In the dries at the Speculator, LaMartine sat quietly on the bench, too tired to put on his street clothes. The rescue crews came in to start the night shift, all of them talking about Duggan's group as they prepared for a long shift underground. He caught snippets of the conversations.

"Surprising that bulkhead weren't far from the Granite Mountain shaft..."

"We was there yesterday evening, passed that very drift. Couldn't see your nose."

"They'd be dead men if the air hadn't cleared..."

"Haven't found Duggan yet. Damnedest thing, they said he was there and then gone."

"They're sending teams into the north country looking for him. Probably where we'll be going..."

LaMartine was exhausted and disturbed at not locating men on the 2200. Before he had come back with Rabs, rescuers found George Gorrie, the shift boss on the 2400 Edith May. His body was only two hundred feet from the 24 station in a drift to the west, with fourteen men on the ground behind him. It was clear Gorrie had gathered them from the stopes and they were following him, rushing to escape, but they were mowed down by the gas from the Granite Mountain as they ran.

And Moore, the shifter for the 2200, and all the men from his stopes, where were they?

His mind was a jumble. The mine was huge, there were so many places men might be. In the urgent push to explore the levels, he had been pulled away from one area after another to check something new, and it left him frustrated, with places left unchecked. All around him was the urgency to find living men, not bodies. Duggan's group had appeared out of nowhere and renewed hope, but finding Gorrie and the bleakness of the 2800 had flattened that.

He thought of the brattice at the end of the *2254. Why would a tunnel be blocked that far back? If somebody was going to bulkhead, they could have built a quick wall near the entrance of the crosscut. The boards were right there, nails, everything they needed.*

He was too tired to chase tangled dead ends. He had reported it twice. Told them where to look. But that rankled him too, because as best he could tell nobody had checked it. It seemed his reports had been pointless, dead ends lost in the urgency, and all they were finding were bodies.

At home that night LaMartine slept badly, climbing and crawling through dark tunnels, the gas and the hiss of his air valves pressed on him. He woke struggling to breathe. The fire in the pot-bellied stove had gone out and his room stunk with smoke. He opened the window to the cold June night and stood listening. The mines on the hill were lit, but the city was mute and waiting.

CHAPTER TWENTY-EIGHT

WITHOUT PAIN

Shirtless and dirty, Duggan and McAdams were covered with cuts, and sockless boots rattled on their feet. They left the station and retraced their steps back along the 2401 crosscut.

Deep urgency pushed Duggan. He had to get rescuers. The bulkhead was down, there was no bell cord, the men would be stuck at the station and the gas might come again at any time and kill them. His only hope was to go far out to the Snowball vein, climb the manways up to the 2000 level, and follow the ventilation crosscut to the Rainbow shaft. *That's the way*, he thought.

He had visualized it hundreds of times in the dark, planning each move to safety. He had worked there for ten years and been in every part of the workings. Knowing about the dead-end 2471 crosscut had saved the men. And now, all that time as a nipper guided him again, he knew which tunnels to take, which manways to climb.

He tried relighting his lamp. "We got enough oxygen, the lamps should work," Duggan said. But the carbide in the reservoir had melted into a mushy lump clogging the bottom. "You got more carbide?" he asked McAdams.

"No," McAdams whispered hoarsely, his throat dry and cracked, "All gone."

Duggan walked ahead in the darkness. From long practice he tried to place each step from tie to tie on the tracks. If he kept his pace and stride even, he could walk steadily without light. They passed the dead-end drift where the bulkhead had been and headed farther into the north country. McAdams stumbled behind, unable to keep up. Duggan stopped to wait, knowing the man would lose his way without help.

"The B switch is just ahead," he told McAdams. Standing there, he noticed a slight draft and it encouraged him. "It's fresh air, pulling from the Gem. The manways will be clear."

They went ahead. In a few minutes the echoes changed and he could feel the space around him enlarge, then he tripped against the point of the switch rail. "Here, this is the B switch," he said to McAdams. "The 2401 keeps going straight. The 3-B turns right." He felt farther along the wall and his hand hit a keg of water. "Here's some water."

"Need that," rasped McAdams. He shuffled up to Duggan, feeling for the keg.

"No. Don't drink it," said Duggan, "The top is off. It'll have gas in it."

McAdams took a deep drink anyway, water spilling around his filthy face and shoulders. He washed it around in his mouth, and drank again, "Tastes like smoke," he spat and wiped his face.

"Don't take any more, it'll make you sick."

"Don't care." McAdams drank again, retched some of it up and wiped his face.

"That's enough. We got to go," said Duggan.

He knelt down with his hands on the rails. They were cool to the touch. In a few moments running his fingers along the tracks, he found the turn point that slid between the two lines. *There it is*, and followed the guiding curve of the steel, over the intersection of the rails at the frog, knowing the curved track beyond would lead him into the right drift. He felt the hard steel under his hands, the compacted dirt and cool roughness of the ground, seeing in his mind exactly where he was.

He called out, "Come on," and McAdams moved toward his voice. Duggan could hear the other man's breathing and the scraping of his boots, "We'll follow the rails, past the Gem to the Snowball stopes."

They reached the Gem shaft, feeling a cool breeze coming down from the surface. The rails curved to the left and they followed, leaving the ventilation shaft behind and the air became stagnant. Intent on his purpose, he paid it no mind.

The distance seemed to ebb on but finally he stumbled on crossing rails. There was only one place like this, "The C drifts," he said to McAdams behind him. Here, the Snowball vein split and drifts went in different directions. They had mined it out, leaving empty stopes where waste rock was dumped and they blasted lateral tunnels to haul the ore from farther out. It was a confusing area but Duggan knew it well, he worked there six days a week. Four tracks converged from a web of drifts that crossed each other. The 2439C manway was on the other side of the open area, at the entrance to the far drift heading left. He had to find it in the maze, then climb.

He stepped forward, hands outstretched, feeling for the opposite wall. McAdams stumbled along, following the sound of Duggan's boots shuffling on the floor.

There were two manways with ladders, the 2439C was to his right. He reached the wall and felt for the alcove blasted out of the granite. Gently kicking his foot forward, he hit the timber landing, and felt for the ladder going up to the 22. The one leading down toward the 26 was just to the left. One misplaced foot and he would fall into it.

Waiting at the base of the ladder, Duggan called to McAdams, "Here it is. Keep your hand on the right wall. The opening going down to the 2600 is to your left. Don't fall."

McAdams came over slowly and stood next to Duggan, panting. His head was throbbing now, but he was fixated on getting out. Duggan struck one of his last matches and it flared, lighting McAdam's sweat-creased cheeks and forehead. His eyes had a far-away stare, and he looked dully at the match with the flame wavering and burning. Then the match went out.

They ain't burning right, Duggan thought. He said to McAdams, "You see the ladder?" McAdams grunted.

The air sat heavy, smelling of tar and slightly sweet. He couldn't figure it out, there should be a draft coming down the manway from the Rainbow, just like at the Gem. Instead, there was a faint odor, but he fought to recall what it was. The only thought in his whole consciousness was getting up the ladders to the 2000. It was a long climb.

"Four hundred feet," Duggan said. "You ready?"

McAdams felt sick to his stomach and his mind rolled uncertainly. He leaned onto the wall to steady himself. "The water," he said to Duggan.

"You okay?" There was no answer.

Duggan swung onto the ladder and began climbing. In a half minute, he was twenty feet up. "Come on Joseph," he called down to McAdams, and continued climbing.

McAdams held unsteadily onto the bottom of the ladder. He tried to shake the feeling off and started up, mechanically moving his arms, then his feet. He lost count of the ladder rungs a few feet up from the floor.

A wave of nausea swept through him, stomach heaving, and he lost his grip on the ladder. Grasping wildly into the empty dark, he fell and floated for an instant, then sharply hit the opposite wall with his back and landed heavily on the floor. Breathing shallowly and lying motionless, his mind spun in the blackness.

He struggled to understand, then muttered "*Gas...*" The air in the manway was bad, and somewhere back in his mind he remembered that when men died of gas poisoning, they drifted into a sleep without pain.

Without pain, the words spun gently. His hand reached up, stretching to touch the bottom of the ladder and his fingers closed gently around the rung for a moment, then slowly fell to the ground.

Eighty feet above, Duggan was breathing heavily as he labored to pull himself up another crosspiece. His head pounded and he stopped on a landing, but it did not help. His arms and legs hardly worked. Even while resting, the fatigue increased. *We took the gambler's chance,* he thought.

"We can make it," he called down the ladder to his companion, but McAdams was lying below, snoring now, dying from the carbon monoxide.

Duggan pulled himself up another rung and cursed, *I'm getting tired*, but he knew he was near the next level.

Up to the 2000, then a long swing west, keep on the tracks, but it was too hard to remember and the images blurred together. He thought of Madge. His right hand slipped and for an instant he almost fell.

He was far up the ladders, nearly one hundred twenty feet, just eighty more to the 2200. Another climb, then an easy walk and the air would be good. He put his hand on his pounding forehead. *So tired*... He stuck his left leg through the crosspiece so he was wedged in and he hung there for a few moments, as a softness suffused his awareness and his eyes slowly shut.

Dear Madge, I have not confided my fears to anyone, have looked and looked for hope only, but if the worst comes I myself have no fears but welcome death with open arms, as it is the last act we all must pass through, and as it is but natural, it is God's will. We should have no objection.

He hung there, arms and legs stuck through the ladder and lost consciousness. His breathing slowed, his heartbeat gentle until it was barely perceptible, and finally, it stopped and he was left ... without pain.

To my dear wife and mother:
It takes my heart to be taken from you so suddenly and unexpectedly, but think not of me, for if death comes, it will be in a sleep without suffering.
I ask forgiveness for any suffering or pain I have caused.
Madge, Dear, the house is for you and the child.
Manus

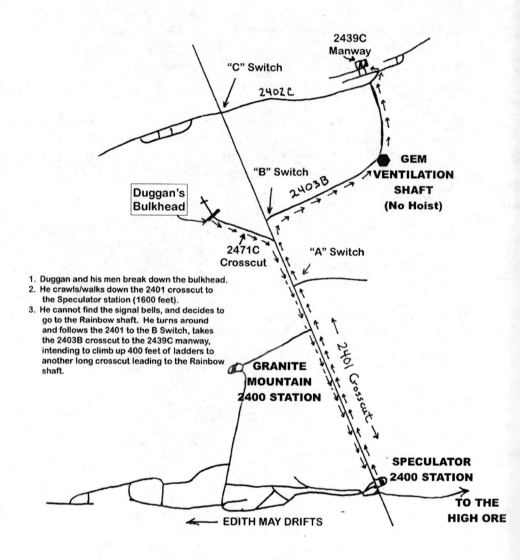

Duggan's breakout from the bulkhead, path to the
Speculator, and attempt to escape north climbing the 2439C
manway to the Rainbow shaft

CHAPTER TWENTY-NINE

FINAL HOURS

By Sunday night, Moore fought to fill his lungs. Sullivan mumbled and repeated, "God have mercy. God have mercy." Moore had forgotten to wind his watch and it had stopped. Time was marked only by labored breaths. Marthey tried to drink the water, but it had taken on the vile stench of the air around them and he could not keep it down. The men moaned, fidgeting as sharp bits of rock in the mud bit into their skin. The blood mixed with the smearing muck in their hair and across their bodies.

As the hours ebbed into Monday, they spoke in low broken phrases, tormented by the slurry of blackness, bad air, mud, and pain that surrounded them. Moore had started to drift, coughing badly, his lungs aching. Marthey lay next to him near the bulkhead.

Laszkeics said to nobody, "I want to die."

Moore roused himself, "You can't give up. Think of your wife, your children. You can live."

The darkness isolated each man, pressing down and overwhelming his hope and life force. The simplest actions took more energy than they could muster. Garrity crawled to the water and tried to turn the stopcock but his fingers were too weak. He could only run his fingers over the faucet, smear several drops of water and bring the moisture to his lips.

Moore was in and out of consciousness, and in the early morning he confided to Marthey, "I'm not going to make it. My lungs are gone."

"Jimmy, you'll make it. You're the toughest man here."

Moore whispered back, "You're young. Help the others."

***

Sometime later Lisa woke with a sense of clarity. Everyone else was asleep. Around him, the dark pressed in and he heard the men's shallow wheezing, a groan here and there.

205

His thoughts flowed together. It was impossible to know how long they had been in the chamber. For much of the time he had been terrified, but now, his fear of death was gone. In its place was a piercing sorrow that he would never see light again. That he would die here with his brothers, lost in an ocean of darkness and rock.

With my brothers, he thought. *We will turn back into dust.*

He yearned for something he could hold onto in this silence and placed his hand on the lower step of the bulkhead. The simple movement was almost more than he could summon. He lay there looking into the dark and seeing images of his homeland, of when he was small on the tiny farm, riding with his father in the wagon, his mother with her embroidery. Other images, of him waving to his parents, leaving to come on the long journey to America, to the mines here. Life stacked up and wove together, as if he could reach across the miles and years and speak to these people.

Lying beside Lisa, Moore stirred and panted. He opened his eyes to the darkness, driven by thoughts of his wife. *For my Pet,* Moore thought. *Some of the men will live. They must know what I want to tell her.*

He gathered his strength, raised himself up and spoke aloud, "I have something to say. I won't make it out of here, but you will. You are my witnesses, in case my notes aren't found." He took a labored breath. "My wife, she gets our life savings, the house, it's hers to sell. Everything I own is hers. She must use it to take care of herself."

Several of the men mumbled in response. Lisa could hear Garrity's voice repeating the sentences, and then Lisa spoke, touching Moore's arm, "We hear, Mr. Moore. We witness for you."

"Okay," Moore whispered. "I'm all in," and he slumped down, unable to hold himself against the bulkhead.

Lisa lightly rested his hand on Moore's shoulder, then drifted to sleep for some time, he didn't know how long. His body felt drained and weak, but his mind was clear. He felt all the other men's lives close around him, bonded together in this chamber that would be their tomb. He had ceased fighting and prayed softly,

"Our Father, who art in Heaven, hallowed be thy Name...," "Forgive me for my sins..."

His prayers were interrupted by distant sounds, and he thought he heard muffled voices, but he was not sure. There was a loud crack, the bulkhead shook and flecks of mud sprinkled down on him.

"Hello, out there," Lisa called.

A voice from outside answered and he spoke with it, telling the voice his name and Moore's, and his brothers' names.

How grateful he was that someone knew they were there. That they would not die alone. After all the struggle, he smiled, and the clear thread holding him there started slipping away, thinner and thinner.

The clarity increased like a pure tone. His brothers were here and they would be saved, and he asked the voice from outside, "Do you have a light? Please, let me see it." Finally, in all the darkness, a light. The light shone and opened up, and he marveled and said, "Thank you."

CHAPTER THIRTY

THE RESCUE

LaMartine was out of his house before dawn, determined to check the bulkhead again. He went to the Speculator, but left his helmet in the dries and headed for the shaft.

"22," he said to the topman, who rang the bells to lower the cage.

"Where's your helmet?" asked the topman.

LaMartine shrugged, "Don't need it yet."

Below, he got off the cage and the station tender greeted him, "Hey Tom."

"Checking something. Back in a bit."

The tender lifted his hand to stop, "The gas, you can't..."

"Don't worry." LaMartine lit his lamp and was gone.

He took the 2202 drift north, following the same route he had used the previous two days. There was still gas in places, but he watched the flame of his lamp closely, and its flutters and brightness told him where the worst had settled. His heart beat wildly as the drifts passed quickly under his feet.

All his senses were sharp. The pinching goggles and constant hiss of the breathing tubes were gone. As he walked, he went through each detail he had seen, imagining what happened. They tumbled out, linking together like a chain.

Walking quickly along the drift, he envisioned how the smoke first appeared and the workers on the sill smelled it, yelling the alarm as they realized there was a fire. *They must have run through the drifts and called out warnings. Others heard and started running. Goodell's men were near the Speculator station and they got out quickly, hoisted up the Spec shaft or through the High Ore.*

Coming up on the 2275 crosscut to the Granite Mountain station, he remembered the four bodies he had found buried in the caved-in rubble by the shaft. *The men working closest to the crosscut ran to the Granite station to be hoisted. They must have*

208.

gotten there just as the smoke and gas started coming from the shaft.

He paused at the junction of the 2202 drift and the 2275 crosscut. The bodies of the motorman and swamper had been sprawled out here. On Sunday, he and Rabs found the motor and loaded train farther back, all the way at the end of the 2202 drift. *Somebody had to run back from here to spread the alarm. The motorman left the ore train and ran for the station, but by that time, the smoke already filled the crosscut and they ran straight into it.*

He looked at where the bodies had been. *The gas came so fast even men on the sill could only get to here....*

LaMartine continued toward the area with the short runs and drifts, knowing he was in Moore's beat. *What would Moore have done?*

Every shift boss knew exactly where his miners were working. *Moore would have spread the alarm in here, gathered the men and tried to lead them out. He would have climbed to his boys in the stopes, ten or twenty floors up, the places hardest to escape from.*

LaMartine sucked his breath through his teeth, thinking of the race against time. He walked past the short runs and drifts, and stopped at the 48 manway, looking up the dark, narrow ladder.

Some of them must have come out here. They would have been slower, maybe the last ones on the sill.

The pieces clicked together in his mind – *did they come down after the motorman and swamper had run by? Did they step straight into the gas?*

Everything started coming together. He went quickly, carbide lamp held out in front of him. His boots scraped the rocky floor, kicking up small puffs of soot. His breathing was even and deliberate. *When they came down, was the gas so bad they could not get past the crosscut to the Spec? Were they cut off from escape?*

He came to the ore car and stopped, looking carefully at the boards fallen across the rails. For the first time, he realized they had fallen back into the tunnel. *Were they knocked down by men rushing into the crosscut?*

He stood looking. *If the gas was already here, Moore would have had to drive the men back to find good air.*

He circled slowly past the ore car, just inside the entrance to the crosscut, and looked carefully at the floor. Crouching down, he picked up one of the sooty nails strewn on the ground and held it in his hand. There was a hammer a few feet farther, next to the track.

This was what had puzzled him the day before. *If men bulkheaded, why didn't they build it here, just inside the entrance? They had the tools, boards, and a good place.* Then he remembered Gorrie, cut down with fourteen men as they ran, and he realized, *They didn't have time. The gas was already on them.*

LaMartine stood there smelling the gassy air and knowing he only had a few minutes. His slight dizziness showed it was already affecting him, building up in his blood stream.

He looked again at the silken ash on the floor and his boot tracks from the last two days. Without the oxygen hissing in the tubes, he heard the silence of the empty tunnels. *Where are the missing men? Are they on this level? Nobody's rapped on the rails, nobody's answered me.*

He yelled into the darkness, "Where are you?"

Forcing the frustration away, he bent down and picked up one of the fallen boards, and it all began to fit.

They were cut off by the gas coming from the crosscut. They rushed back here, grabbed lagging boards, tools, and spilled all these nails. Moore must have thought they could build a blind here. But they couldn't. They had to go in farther.

LaMartin started back into the 2254 crosscut, carrying the board. He saw another lagging board fallen to the side, ash on its surface, and glanced up at the canvas pipe hangers dangling loosely on the overhead timbers.

They stripped down the canvas piping as they ran.

His steps came faster and certainty welled up.

They had to keep going to get into good air.

He hurried, aware of the charcoal-singed taste in his mouth and felt the gas chasing him.

It was in on them. They had no choice.

He felt the franticness and fear. He was running now, his

210

steps tight and clipped.

They ran until there was nowhere left to go.

He came to the bulkhead and stood before it, winded, the smell of burned wood heavy around him.

And they built it ... here. He put his hands on the bulkhead, his breaths heaving. And he knew as he touched it, *There are men behind this.*

The tunnel spun, and his dizziness frightened him. The fans had been clearing the workings for three days, but the carbon monoxide was strong here.

I have to get a crew ..., and oxygen.

LaMartine hurried back to the surface and came off the cage single-mindedly. The other groups were there, the Tramway and Anaconda teams, and he saw Rosie talking to Budelier.

Hurrying across the yard to the dries, the shift boss Eticker flagged him down, "Tom, we been looking all over for you. Rosie needs a guide."

LaMartine brushed the order away and asked, "You got a map?"

"Uh, yeah but we got to..."

"Show it to me."

LaMartine followed him into the office, squeezing past the timekeeper and clerks.

Eticker pulled out a map, "This ain't great, but it shows most of the west side."

"Let me look."

LaMartine unrolled it on the desk. "I found this brattice in the west Spec 22 country. Right here. This 54 crosscut." He tapped his finger on the spot. "Reported it yesterday, and Saturday too. Been two days and nobody's looked. We need to tear it down. Now."

Eticker looked hard at the map, "Huh, yeah, okay we'll look into that."

"No, I need help right now." LaMartine insisted.

"Well ..."

"Now!"

"Okay, okay. Hey Turk!"

211

The young office clerk looked up from the desk, "Yeah?"

"Take LaMartine over to the Granite Mountain in the machine, I'm calling Braly, he's in the office there. Show him the map, see what he says."

LaMartine thought to himself, *I'm going back down whether they want me to or not.*

Turk cranked the Model T's starter out in the yard. It jerked and chattered, belched out a backfire, then settled into a rough chugging. He jumped in and motioned to LaMartine, "Come on!" He screeched it into gear, and the car clattered past the buildings. The guards opened the gate and the crowd of people parted to let them through, bouncing down the road toward the Granite Mountain mineyard.

Braly was waiting in the office, with a map of the 2200 spread out. He had deep rings under his eyes. The last three days were etched deeply on his face.

He shook LaMartine's hand, "Eticker called, said there's something you want me to look at?"

LaMartine looked the stope map over, the drifts and crosscuts were finely drawn with a draftsman's hand, manways marked and numbered, veins colored in. Around the tunnels were penciled markings for the direction of air currents and where bodies had been found. "There's a heavy built bulkhead, back in..." he traced down the drifts, "... here," he said, his finger near the end of the 2254.

Braly bent over the map, "Yeah, I know the crosscut. We're driving over to the Adirondack vein from the Edith May. They hit ore a couple of weeks ago, had two assays, we're running a drift north at the end."

LaMartine broke in, "I been there three times. The bulkhead is maybe four hundred feet in from the switch, all the way at the end. Thrown up from the blind side. You got anything like that?"

Braly shook his head, "No, there's nothing in there."

"Well, there is now."

"Can't be." Braly said flatly, ready to dismiss LaMartine.

LaMartine looked Braly in the eye, "There is. I had my

212

hands on it."

"Well, it's either put in there for ventilation purposes, or else it has been put in there since the fire by rescuers."

"Nobody's been in there but me," said LaMartine. "No tracks, just ash and soot on the floor. If it wasn't there before the fire, then it had to be built..." he leaned forward, "... during the fire." Braly and LaMartine stared at the 2254.

"Let's go," said Braly.

He called rescue and ordered a crew down to the 2200. LaMartine and Braly were joined by Mike Bezick and two other helmet men. LaMartine picked up an axe and hefted it, thinking, *I'm going to be ready.* They jumped on the cage.

On the 2200 they put their helmets on, and he led them inside the workings, back through the long tunnels and maze of short runs and drifts. He cautioned them about the lingering gas. They reached the fan and he steered them into the long crosscut. As they went, Braly began to doubt and pulled out his mouthpiece, "Wouldn't you throw up a blind before this? Back at the entrance?" LaMartine did not answer and kept walking fast, the others twenty steps behind, until he stood at the bulkhead, well constructed, thick and solid, with the boards nailed tight.

Braly caught up and said, "I don't know, Tom. This doesn't look like something guys just threw up."

LaMartine said, "I'm taking it down." He lifted the axe and swung hard and smooth and tore a board off. The piece flipped through the air with dirt flying. He hefted the axe again and reared back.

But from inside came a voice, firm and clear, "Hello out there."

LaMartine's breath stopped. He lowered the axe head and answered the voice, "How are you? Alright?"

"Yes, we're alright, but the air is bad."

"How many of you in there?"

"Ten of us."

"Can you hold out another five minutes?"

"I think so, but hurry."

Braly stood listening, speechless. LaMartine turned to him,

"Go to the surface and bring back doctors, water, oxygen. Get rail trucks, bring it all back." Braly rushed off, then LaMartine ordered the two other men, "Go out to the entrance of the crosscut. Get that ore car off the tracks so we can get the rail trucks in here."

The men left. LaMartine took his mouthpiece out and again spoke to the man behind the wall.

"What's your name?"

The voice came clearly, "John Lisa."

"Who is with you?"

"Shifter Moore is here. Clarence Marthey, Martin Garrity, and Mike Sullivan."

The other men started to groan and breath heavily, wakening to the sounds of the conversation.

LaMartine looked at Bezick, "Air must be horrible in there." He reached for the end of a loosened board. "I'm going to open the top of the bulkhead. That'll help them."

He pulled the mud-caked board off, tossing it against the drift wall. A wave of putrid air rolled down from the opening and snuffed their lamps out. LaMartine felt his gorge rush up his throat and choked it back. It took a minute before the air cleared enough so they could relight their lamps. "They got almost no oxygen in there," he said.

LaMartine and Bezick stood beside the bulkhead and the lone voice spoke again, weaker, "Do you have a light?"

"Yes." LaMartine picked up his lamp from the floor.

"Please. Let me see it."

LaMartine pointed it through the break in the top of the bulkhead and shined it onto the back and wall inside. He heard a sigh. "Alright," said the voice softly. "Thank you."

LaMartine waited for several minutes, but it was quiet. The groans of the men behind the bulkhead eased as the outside air passed into the chamber, and the foul air circulated out the top. The stench lessened, and the lamps burned brighter.

Braly came with ten men, pushing two rail trucks with oxygen and stretchers on them. LaMartine quickly tore the top of the wall down. The boards had shoes, hats, pants, and jackets nailed to them, anything to cover the cracks. It was backed by timbers and waist-high dried mud. *No wonder they couldn't hear me before,* he thought.

He climbed over the broken bulkhead and carefully stepped among the men, who were too frail to move. The rancid air lingered on the floor, smelling of smoke, sweat, and excrement – lifeless air that had been rebreathed a million times.

LaMartine straddled over the remaining timbers. Dim forms lay on the ground, and three men were against the bulkhead. He recognized Moore, slumped over and motionless. LaMartine gently stretched him out and his warm body moved easily, but his face was ashen, and his chest did not rise. He lifted Moore over the broken boards and packed dirt, and handed him to the men and doctors outside.

The small man in the middle was not breathing, but the man next to him turned his head and looked, dazed at the light. LaMartine bent down to the man's face, thinking it was Lisa, and said, "We'll get you out of here."

He carried the man over the rubble and said to the other rescuers, "I'm taking him up to the surface," and set off through the tunnels to the Speculator station. There, he held the man on the chippy cage, sweat dripping down, and the tender rang three bells to be raised. It seemed endless coming up the long shaft, but the crowd shouted when LaMartine appeared out of the cage holding a limp but alive man under his arms. Two doctors gently took him.

LaMartine stood drained, mouthpiece dangling down, watching the doctors put the man on a stretcher and hurriedly take him away. *John Lisa is safe,* he thought, relieved, and turned to go back. Boardman, the head of the rescue teams, forced him to stop. "Tom, you can't go until you've taken a break," but within minutes he was on a cage down to the 22.

At the station, Moore was lying on a stretcher surrounded by men, a doctor compressing his chest and an oxygen mask on his face. Unable to help, LaMartine rushed back toward the bulkhead where rescuers were giving the men water and rubbing them with towels.

Inside the bulkhead, rescuers argued with Erickson, who awakened and was terrified. When he saw the tubes and goggles

215

of a helmet man's face, he croaked "Demon!" and cowered backward. When Bezick reached toward him, he yelled, "Get away!" LaMartine put his light outside and took his helmet off. He went to Erickson back in the dark, sat down next to him talking quietly and reassuring him. Finally, he persuaded the man to go out.

Marthey raised his head but could only stare; Truax lay on his back beside him, unmoving. Laszkeics opened his eyes and whispered his name to a rescuer, then fell unconscious. None could stand or even sit up by themselves.

A halting train of men and rail trucks moved along the tracks, there were lights everywhere. LaMartine helped carry Erikson on a stretcher, speaking to him quietly. Soon, all the men were on the surface.

The crowd opened up as each cage of men came. Rescuers held them upright and laid them carefully under the Speculator headframe as the crowd watched in silence. There was none of the happy cheering which had met Duggan's group. The men's plight was too grave and the news of Moore's death had traveled ahead, subduing people who watched the frail figures.

Two died before they could be hoisted. One was Truax. Nobody knew the other one's name. It was the small man who was next to Moore at the bulkhead.

In the fresh air, Garrity revived quickly and was the only one who was able to talk coherently. His eyes were wild and dilated, lips cracked and parched. He kept saying, "Notify my brother at the Pacific Hotel."

He looked up at the rescuers, face creased and haggard but a smile playing on it, "Was hell down there boys, it's great to be up. What day is it? Saturday?"

"Nay, Monday," said a man bending over him.

"Maybe I'll get double time," he said.

The doctors and rescuers nurtured the other men, carefully trying to coax life – strong men made fragile, clutching at survival, entombed then brought back into light.

Marthey was partly conscious. He woke when a rescuer sprinkled cold water on his face, then sipped coffee from a cup brought to his lips. Tongue swollen and throat dry, they loaded him on a stretcher and lifted him into an ambulance. Two men sat next to him to control his thrashing as he fought to rise on his elbows, screaming, "Turn on the air!"

Sullivan woke and sat up, swaying precariously in carbon monoxide paranoia. The rescuers held out a cup for him to drink, smiling and encouraging, but he would not take it. Doctors asked questions, and one leaned over and put his hand on Sullivan's shoulder. He swatted the hand and stared around suspiciously, eyes distrustful, "I'm not giving you my name." A doctor placed some coffee next to him, and he pushed it abruptly away, hissing, "It's poisoned."

Laszkeics woke briefly again but was so weak he could barely nod. He whispered to the doctor, "Please tell my wife ..."

Moore's wife had been called but there was no good news. Sitting by his body she cradled his head, caressing his muddy hair and face.

When the last of the men had been taken to the hospital, LaMartine stood below the Speculator headframe. He pushed his goggles up on his filthy forehead, his eyes were ringed with dust. Crowds of men milled. Braly stood with several news reporters, answering questions and describing the rescue.

Friendly hands slapped LaMartine's shoulders, unknown men embraced him with tears in their eyes – an outpouring of emotion from a city with too much sorrow. He saw Rosie and Budelier come through the crowd. Weigenstein joined them, then Hamill and Goodell, all of them standing together. Three hundred yards away, a thin swirl of smoke rose up from the Granite Mountain shaft.

**Tom LaMartine in the center of the crowd after rescuing
Moore's men.** *Butte Miner,* June 12, 1917.
Used with permission from Butte-Silver Bow Archives.

CHAPTER THIRTY-ONE

THE HOSPITAL

On Saturday, Stanley had not come home, and Helen Laszkeics could get no word about her husband. Her friend Bridget Marcinkowski came to the door knocking, then let herself in. By evening, the family had moved to the Marcinkowski's on South Arizona. They gave Helen their bed to sleep in with the children, while they slept on the porch.

The house was filled with two families. The children played in the bare yard and threw rocks into the street. Those from the neighboring houses came over to see the newcomers, squatting alongside the three-year olds, intent on a game no adult could ever understand. Helen helped in the kitchen and fed the twins while holding the baby.

The children accepted that their father was not going to be home soon. Helen feared more bad news was coming, a fear that grew with each passing hour until it loomed through all her thoughts.

Near noon on Monday there was a loud knock on the door and Helen went to answer with the baby in her arms. Before she could get from the kitchen to the door there was a second, then a third pounding. Impatiently, she swung the door wide open with a scowl, "What do you want?"

It was Frank Sczynansky, her husband's friend from the mine. "Helen, they have found Stanley. He's alive!"

"Oh, what are you saying?" her heart began to pound.

"They have brought him up!"

"Where is he?"

"The hospital! Rescuers found him."

She stared at Frank as if what he said could not be true. Mrs. Marcinkowski came quickly from a back room, "What is this?"

"Stanley is in the hospital!" Frank shouted.

"Let me have the child, Helen," said Bridgett. "You must go!"

Helen fled through the door, running with all her might. All the emotion she had been struggling to hold rushed out in one thought, *I must see him.*

Her shoes fell off her feet, but she did not even feel them as she dashed to St. James Hospital. Up Arizona Street she went, then turned west along Porphyry Street, past warehouses and ramshackle cabins tacked onto houses. Her hair unraveled in tendrils down her back. Her dress caught on a fence and she yanked it, ripping the hem away.

He is alive!

She dodged a horse-drawn buggy, then a truck swerved as the driver honked loudly. She paid no mind but ran as fast as she could over wet cobblestones and horse manure, and she angled to the side with the hospital a few blocks ahead, just up on Silver Street. Rushing around the end of a trolley car on Main, she nearly collided with a wagon, startling the driver. "Whoa Ma'am!" he pulled the reins, "What are you...?" But she was already gone.

She ran up the hospital steps and through the doors to the clerk at the desk, her looks shouting everything that she had hidden the last three days. "Tell me what room Stanley Laszkeics is in."

The clerk found it, "Second floor, 210."

Stanley lay on the bed motionless and she picked up his hand, cradling it, putting it to her cheek and then her lips. Helen knelt by his side and leaned her face close to his. He slowly opened his eyes. His lips trembled and a weak smile formed. Tears trickled down his cheeks and she brushed them with her fingertips.

"I love you," she said softly and whispered in Polish, "*Kocham Cię.*"

CHAPTER THIRTY-TWO

THE LIGHT

Tuesday morning the city was filled with stories about the rescue. On the front page of the newspaper there was a list of the men in Moore's bulkhead. LaMartine read the names of the living and the dead, but could not find Lisa. The article said that four men died during the rescue, Moore, Truax, and two who were unidentified. John Lisa was not mentioned.

LaMartine was confused, and thought back to the bulkhead. *Lisa was the one I talked to. He was strong and knew everyone's name. I carried him out.*

He went the hospital, visiting with each of the survivors and listening closely for the voice he had heard. Erickson was recovering, and he found Marthey walking down the hall helped by his wife. Garrity's room was filled with his joyous friends. The young mucker Knutti smiled, grateful to be alive.

Laszkeics sat upright in his bed, propped by blankets, his wife Helen beside him, holding his hand. Stanley thanked LaMartine in a low whisper. "I wanted to die but Moore wouldn't let me. Now, I am alive and he is dead." Helen squeezed his hand and wiped his eyes.

None of the men's voices matched the one from the other side of the bulkhead, but when he reached Sullivan's room, LaMartine stood at the door, gazing at his face. It was the man he had lifted out of the bulkhead and carried to the surface.

"How are you? Alright?" asked LaMartine, sitting down beside him.

The man's eyes opened and he looked at LaMartine, "Yes, I'm alright."

"What's your name?"

"Mike Sullivan."

"I saw you in the mine. You were up against the bulkhead."

TOM LA MARTINE.

living after 60 hours in the mine
were:
Martin Garrity, Pacific hotel.
Emil Knutti, 827½ East Galena
street.
Mike Sullivan, 125 Boardman
street.
Stanley Lazykeics, 10 Clark street.
Clarence Maithey, 147 Wing street,
Meaderville.
Ole T. Erickson, South Arizona
street.
Those rescued who died later are:
Robert Truax, Florence hotel.
J. D. Moore, 426 North Alabama
street.
Two unidentified men.

Manus Duggan Lost.

No trace has been found of Manus
Duggan, who led 29 men to safety,
and all hope of finding him alive
has been given up.
The task of burying the dead was

June 12, 1917, Tom LaMartine and list of men from Moore's bulkhead. Front page, *Anaconda Standard. Used with permission from Butte-Silver Bow Archives.*

222

Sullivan struggled to remember, "I was with shifter Moore."

"There was another man there, a small man beside you."

"Lisa. It was John Lisa," said Sullivan. He breathed quietly for a while, "How is he?"

LaMartine's thoughts rushed together, all his certainty about what had happened, his relief after saving Lisa. He remembered the list in the newspaper, the two unidentified men who died. But he had picked up Sullivan, not Lisa.

LaMartine stumbled for words, "I think, he didn't make it."

Sullivan groaned, his eyes blinking through tears.

A nurse came in, "Only a minute. He is frail."

"Yes, of course," LaMartine stood up. Sullivan held out his hand, weak and shaking, and LaMartine took it into his.

"I carried you up to the surface," he said, and their eyes met again.

"Thank you," said Sullivan.

He left the hospital, and a deep sadness washed through him. He had been so sure Lisa would live. After touching so much death, he wanted to see him alive.

Lisa sounded so strong, but there is a limit to what men can stand. He was dying as they spoke, falling away from LaMartine and his brothers at the bulkhead, even as he was being rescued.

He asked if I had a light and I showed him. He thanked me, and those were his last words.

***

Early on Monday, Martin Garrity's brother Ed had identified a body he thought was Martin, but he was not certain and returned to the Speculator's morgue. He arrived just after Moore's group had been brought to the surface and taken to the hospital. Somebody told him his brother was alive, and he rushed down into the city.

In the hospital room he cried, "Is it really Martin? Oh, Martin my boy, you're really saved!"

Friends spread the word and Garrity's landlady at the Pacific Hotel put a tab on the saloon next door for all who wanted to drink to his health. Hundreds of fellow miners came, and the whiskey and laughter flowed freely. She was enthusiastic, "I'd rather spend twenty dollars setting up the drinks to celebrate the return to life of Garrity than five dollars of flowers for his wake!"

The Anaconda Standard.

VOL. XVIII—No. 282.   ANACONDA, MONTANA, TUESDAY MORNING, JUNE 12, 1917.   PRICE FIVE CENTS.

TEN BUTTE MINERS ENDURE THE LIMIT OF EXHAUSTION BUT FOUR OF THEM EXPIRE JUST AFTER HELP COMES

ANOTHER HERO GIVES HIS LIFE

BRAVE SHIFT BOSS AT SPECULATOR MINE DIES JUST AS RESCUE COMES

BENEFACTORS MOURN

His struggles and encouragement give strength to eight men whom he pilots to safety—He expires while being placed in cage—He writes to friends and relatives while yet light remains near the bulkhead—Wife, mother and brothers survive—Had been here three years.

James D. Moore, shift boss in the Speculator, after valiantly keeping life in eight men who were with him on the 2,400-foot level and who had periled unconsciousness until a few minutes before help reached them, died, when lifted on the cage to carry him to safety.

[body text illegible]

JAMES D. MOORE.

IT'S HOT.

Topeka, Kan., June 11.—All heat records for 1917 in Kansas were shattered today when the thermometer registered 92 degrees for the third straight day.

In Today's Standard

[index column illegible]

GREAT CONCOURSE FOLLOWS FIVE HEARSES

THEIR RESCUE IS UNEXPECTED

AND ONCE AGAIN THERE COMES A RAY OF HOPE THAT OTHERS ARE ALIVE

BUT IT'S ONLY SLIGHT

[body text illegible]

SULLAU IN DYING WORD TOOK BLAME FOR FIRE

Assistant Foreman Whose Lamp Set Fire to Cable Asked That He Be Held Responsible, Some Incidents of the Fire as Told by Some of the Survivors.

[body text illegible]

LARGE FUNERAL CORTEGE FIVE OF FIRE VICTIMS

[body text illegible]

LIST OF IDENTIFIED DEAD AND THOSE RESCUED ALIVE

[body text illegible]

MRS. DUGGAN STILL HOPES AND WAITS FOR HUSBAND

[body text illegible]

MARTIN GARRITY TELLS STORY OF EXPERIENCE

"It's Too Bad That Moore Couldn't Have Lived; He Saved Us."

[body text illegible]

TOM LA MARTINE.

A NORTH BUTTE OFFICER WILL ARRIVE HERE TODAY

[body text illegible]

ALBINO MASSA.

WEATHER FORECAST.

Washington, June 11.—Forecast: Montana: Partly cloudy Tuesday; Wednesday fair and warmer.

(Continued on Page 11, Column 3.)

CHAPTER THIRTY-THREE

THE TROLLEY

Everyone knew that Duggan was lost. There was only the waiting dread that comes after hope is gone.

Shift boss Budelier found two bodies in the stopes out in the north country. Duggan had been his nipper in earlier years, and it was a personal battle for him to help. He was certain that one of the bodies was Manus and reported that, but the state of the body made it impossible to tell.

Madge's brother arrived at the mine office to identify it but despite Budelier's earnestness, a fine silver watch was found in the pocket of the poor man, "This is not Manus," said the brother. The watch was set out for the man's family members to identify.

On June 14, Duggan's body was found by shift boss Hamill, on a ladder in the 2439C manway. They identified it by the letters carefully folded in his pockets.

Thousands of people came to the service, packing the church and surrounding it outside. Afterwards, Madge stepped out, heavy with child. She saw all the people and began sobbing. The procession stretched along the street for half a mile as it wound to St. Patrick's Cemetery.

On Duggan's gravestone was written:
No greater love hath any man than that he shall lay down his life for his friend.
John 15:13

***

In July, their child was born. A little girl with her father's warm friendly eyes. Madge named her Manus.

***

November, 1917
On a chilly autumn day late in the afternoon, Madge stepped out of a bakery on Park Street, going home to make dinner.

She swaddled her baby against the brisk wind until only the child's face showed. A westbound trolley stopped, then she climbed onto it, the baby in one arm, bread and groceries in the other.

"Here, let me help, Ma'am," said a miner. She thanked him and sidled into the aisle, giving the conductor her fare. Two dirt-covered men sat in the first seats, crumpled hats on their heads, carrying their carbide miner's lamps and lunch buckets. Their tired faces softened into smiles as they stood to make a place for her.

"Please...," they gestured at the now open bench. The car was packed with working men, some staring out the window at the gray evening, others sitting with their jacket collars turned up and eyes closed. Half-burned candles stuck out of pockets.

One of the men who had made a place for Madge stood in the aisle, holding onto the bar above. He peered at her face and at the child, then nudged the other and whispered something, nodding toward Madge. The men around them looked up, eyes drawn to the slight woman cradling the baby in her arms, until a dozen men were gazing at her.

The first man timidly looked down at his feet, a bit embarrassed. Then with an earnest face he stepped up to Madge and said softly, "Mrs. Duggan, may I hold the child?"

Men whispered to each other through the trolley, "It's Duggan's wife and the child."

One after the other nodded, and they stood up in twos and threes, taking their hats off. The first man reached out shyly, his hands calloused and dirty from shoveling ore. The other men shuffled closer down the aisle to take their turn, faces smudged, but eyes open and alive.

Nothing was said as the baby passed from miner to miner, their coarse hands cradling the sleeping infant with tenderness, gazing at the sleeping girl as Madge Duggan watched. When the baby was handed back, her blanket was smeared with grit and dust from the working hands of the miners.

"Thank you, Ma'am," said the first man, holding his hat in his hand. And the trolley rocked up the cobblestone street into the evening.

Glossary

Mining is filled with technical terms and slang. Some of the terms in the book were particular to the early 1900s and are no longer used.

Levels underground – In the Speculator, the numbers that designate the levels underground were usually in 200 foot increments. In 1917, the mine's working levels started at the 400 foot level, down to the 3700 foot level. The larger the number, the deeper the level, and they were typically referred to in shortened form. For example, the 2400-foot level is called "the 24", and so forth.

18 = 1800	24 = 2400
20 = 2000	26 = 2600
22 = 2200	28 = 2800

Apparatus men – A name for rescuers using early primitive breathing devices like "**Helmets**", which are the **Fleuss** or **Dreger** apparatus.

Back – The roof or ceiling of a tunnel. Miners don't use "ceiling".

Big Cages – Larger cages that carried seven to nine men, which are put on the main shaft and hauled by the main hoist in place of skips at shift change. These usually consisted of four stacked cages, one on top of the other, and all four filled with men would be lifted or lowered at once.

Blacksmith – Men who worked with metal. Every major Butte mine had extensive blacksmith and carpentry shops. Riveting together ore cars, chains, some actually wove steel hoist cables with specialized machines. constructing towers, sharpening the steel drill bits, working with foundries to make specialized metal parts.

Brattice (also **Blind** or **Bulkhead**) – Walls constructed in a tunnel to control ventilation out of boards and canvas. They are usually not airtight, but if backed by mud or concrete, they can be.

Bulkhead – (see also **Brattice, Blind**) A heavier form of a brattice or blind, built to seal out air flow. In mining practice, they usually have a opening door, which can be wooden, or iron.

Buzzie – A smaller type of drill run by compressed air.

Cable – the hoists used woven steel cables thousands of feet long to attach to the cages and skips. Standard for the Chippy hoist was one-inch thick cable, while for the main hoist it was 1¾ inch cable, which was capable of holding far more than 60,000 pounds of weight without breaking.

Cage – A metal open carrying platform, with metal side sheets, on which men and some equipment are raised or lowered down the shaft. (Also, see **Skips** – Steel bins used to haul several tons of ore or waste rock up the shaft).

Cage tenders – Men assigned to move with a cage, either on the chippy or the "big cages" for lifting shifts. They controlled loading and unloading of ore, equipment, or men, and only they could ring the hoist engineer.

Canvas piping (see Fan pipe)

Chippy hoist – A secondary single-drum service hoist used to raise or lower men and materials while the main hoist was bringing up rock.

Chute – A small vertical shaft in a stope, perhaps three feet by three feet, used to drop ore down from above, and walled off with planks. As miners worked upward in a vein, they built a timber scaffolding with floors every eight feet, connected by ladders and chutes. Ore was excavated from the vein and dropped down the chutes between levels, ending with steel gates at the bottom which, when opened, allowed the ore to fall into a one-ton rail car.

Compressed air – The standard driving force for rock drills, at 90 pounds per square inch pressure, because it can be piped long distances and retain nearly all of its force, unlike steam. Large coal-fired, steam compressor plants were used on virtually all mines, but were being replaced in 1917 by electric compressor motors.

Country rock (or **waste rock**)– Granite rock without ore.

Crosscut – A horizontal underground tunnel that crosses veins at an angle, used by men and by rail cars to reach tunnels along the ore veins (see **Drifts**). It typically goes through **country rock** from the shaft to intersect one or more veins, or to connect drifts. In the Speculator Mine, the Granite Mountain shaft was built in much more solid rock than the Speculator shaft. From it, the miners drove a second major crosscut that paralleled the crosscut from the Speculator shaft. Mines typically drove crosscuts out at intervals from each shaft parallel to each other (see map) so they crossed multiple veins at different places. Where they crossed a vein, another tunnel, a **Drift**, was driven along the ore vein and used for access by the men, compressed air lines (for drills), and rail motors to haul back ore.

Downcast shaft – A shaft through which air comes into the mine for ventilation.

Draeger- (see also **Helmet, Fleuss, Apparatus**) Early type of underwater or self-contained breathing device invented by Heinrich Draeger in the mid-1800s, later adapted to use in mine fires and fire-fighting. It contained a different method of CO_2 scrubbing and injection of oxygen, so a man could breath and rescue in a mine filled with poison gas. The company started by Draeger still exists and is in the forefront of fire-fighting and extreme environment breathing apparatus.

Drift – A horizontal passageway underground that follows an ore vein. As distinguished from a crosscut, which intersects a vein. Miners "drift" along a vein, and build stopes upward to mine out the ore. Drifts are referred to by number and letter, corresponding to the vein, and the rail switch leading to them. They are numbered historically, as the miners work. They typically get larger as they get farther from the shaft, or get farther from the crosscut they originate at.

Face – The exposed area of a vein or ore body from which ore is being extracted

Fan pipe (or **Canvas piping, Fanbag**) – Cloth "pipes" made of heavy canvas to funnel air flow, used to direct air currents to ventilate places off the main air flow between surface openings.

Flat truck – A flat rail car without sides on which men could stack boards or tools or dynamite, and push it to a destination on a level.

Fleuss – (see also **Helmet, Draeger, Apparatus**) Early type of underwater or self-contained breathing device invented by the English diving engineer and inventor Henry Fleuss. Variants of it were used as breathing devices in mining disasters, where rescuers were required to move through poison gas and smoke. Usually they included gas tanks with pressurized oxygen, air, and a CO_2 scrubber. Early forms allowed breathing underwater or in smoke for two hours.

Hangfire – When a burning fuse slows or stops ("hangs"), leading to a dynamite round failing to explode with the proper timing relative to the other rounds. See "**missed round**" or "**missed hole**".

Haulage way – Tunnels with rails specifically used to haul ore away from the drifts and stopes to the shaft to be raised to the surface. Usually the rails were placed the main crosscuts and the drifts.

Headframe – The wooden or steel structure above the shaft that supports the pulleys (Sheave wheels) which guide the hoisting cable vertically into the shaft. See the top of the cover photograph, which shows the Granite Mountain headframe. These could be as small as ten feet high, or as large as t he Granite Mountain headframe – Heavy Eifel Tower-like iron scaffolding over 150 feet tall with five additional idler towers to support the cable. Around 1917, there were more than 50 large headframes across the Butte Hill serving mines.

Helmet men – Rescuers using Fleuss or Draeger breathing apparatus.

Hoist – The main motor and drum arrangement with cable, that lifts and lowers cages, skips, or other loads in the shaft.

Hoist engineer – The man who runs the hoist. Probably one of the hardest jobs, critical in raising and lowering the men, loads of ore or waste rock, timber, dynamite, and all equipment.

Holes – The holes drilled into the working face of a drift, into which dynamite was put to blast the ore free. They were drilled typically from two to six feet deep.

Honey Car – The toilet car. There were several on each working level.

Horsetail – An area where a vein splits into many small veinlets too small to mine individually, but close enough to mine en masse. Thin hair-like veins of ore (see also **Stringer**)

Idler Tower – The secondary towers away from the headframe that keep the cable between the hoist and the sheaves from sagging, whipping, or vibrating excessively.

Jack-leg – A percussion drill used for drifting or stoping, mounted on a telescopic air cylinder that both supports the weight of the drill and feeds it into the rock. The leg and machine are hinged so the drill can be turned in a different direction than the leg, making it versatile.

Missed round or **missed hole** (see also, "**hangfire**")– When the dynamite in one of the holes does not explode, often due to a damaged or wet fuse. This was an extremely dangerous situation, as the dynamite had to be removed, often by carefully chipping away the rock around the hole. Many deaths and maimings occurred when the dynamite went off with men standing near, having come back to check the face.

Motor – A small electric locomotive used to pull ore cars from the drifts to the station.

Muck – After blasting with dynamite, the broken rock containing ore and granite. This can include fine dusty particles up to chunks depending on how hard the rock is. It can also be the sloughing clay-like dirt from a fault.

Muckbound –When more ore and/or waste is being produced than can be hauled away. This can mean a full chute from a stope, or an entire level because there is a problem with the skip pockets, or the entire mine if there is a problem with the shaft or hoist.

Muckers – Men shoveling the broken ore and rock after a blast, down a chute, or loading ore into wheelbarrows or mine cars.

Nippers – Men who delivered tools to the workers, took dull drill bits and returned them from the blacksmith's sharpened to be used again.

Ore – Any of the commercially viable metal ores. These included more than a dozen forms of copper ore, also zinc, silver, lead, manganese. The primary metal was copper, but Butte ores were known for having significant amounts of silver at a wide range of depths, and also gold. In later years they also provided up to 40% of the zinc used in the country.

Ore Pocket (or **Skip Pocket**)– A chamber usually blasted out of rock next to the shaft, into which ore is dumped from the motor trains, and which loads a skip using an automatic (usually hydraulic) gate. Waste rock that had to be lifted out of the mine, or to a different level, also could be put into the pockets to be loaded onto a skip.

Pump or Service compartment – A section of a shaft, set apart on one end, used for services such as compressed air and water pipes, electric cables, and signal bells, and in later years, a ladder for emergency and maintenance. It was open to the Chippy shaft but separated by the supporting cross timbers every six to eight feet. The Granite Mountain pump compartment where the cable was being lowered was three by five feet in size, and did not contain a ladder, nor did the Speculator shaft. After the Speculator disaster, shafts were concreted so the timbers couldn't catch fire and ladders were added to the service compartment.

Raise – A vertical "tunnel" connecting levels. Typically raises had three compartments, a ladderway which men could climb up or down, a chute for hauling timber up, and a chute lined with planks down which ore was dumped to the gates at the bottom. Usually raises were connected directly into stoping areas where there was active mining. Some were left open for ventilation.

Ribs – The walls of a tunnel or stope.

Ropemen – Men who specialized in handling the cables in the shaft for hoisting cages and skips, or raising and lowering other cables, pipes, and materials, such as the electrical cable that started the fire in the Granite Mountain shaft. They also worked with all ropes with pulleys, internal hoists, and winches.

Runners/guides – On opposite sides of the inside of the shaft there were guides made of teak hardwood that kept cages or skips guided and aligned in the shaft as they were raised or lowered. The teak resisted the temperature, constant wear, acidic water, humidity, and condensation. A substantial part of the world's teak forests ended up in Butte mines as guides in shafts two to five thousand feet deep.

Shaft – The opening from the surface down into the mine. Both the Speculator and Granite Mountain shafts had four compartments, including the pump compartment. The oldest shafts on the hill were a single compartment with a horse or man-turned winch. In the years

1875-1885 most mines used two hoisting compartments, because the hoists used were counterbalanced – one side went up while the other side went down. By the early 1900s most mines had three hoisting compartments, two for lifting ore, or lifting groups of men during shift changes, and one as a separate hoist (the **chippy**) for smaller groups or even individual men and materials. The main hoist was akin to a dump truck or bus, the chippy was equivalent to a cab. There also was a fourth compartment, the **pump compartment**. The main compartments were approximately five feet by five feet, and the pump compartment was about three feet by five feet in most mines after 1888 or so.

Shaft Collar – The opening of the shaft at the surface under the headframe.

Shaftman – Men who specialized in dealing with sinking, construction, and repair of the shafts, including the wooden guides for the cages and skips.

Shift boss – A boss in charge of from ten to fifty miners working in stopes; it would include all the men working, nippers, timbermen and miners, motormen, station tenders, as well as contractors.

Sill – The floor of a working place. Usually used with respect to the main drift or haulage-way. For example, one might enter a stope on the 2400 sill, then climb up the floors (usually 28 floors between 200 foot levels) and come out on the sill on the 2200.

Skip – The large steel box-like conveyance attached to the hoist cable that holds ore when it is raised up the shaft. A skip could be fifteen feet high and hold ten tons of ore or waste rock.

Skip tenders/cage tenders – Men assigned to move with the skips or cages. They ran the bells to the hoist engineer.

Slag – The melted and reconstituted non-metal elements left from smelting when the sulfides have had all the metals removed by heat and chemical recombination. Basically forms of silica and granite minerals remelted and then cooled.

Stamp mill – A mill with giant steel stamps that crushed ore into tiny particles, which then were put through machines using gravity to separate metallic particles from waste, the second stage of mechanically separating the ore from the waste rock. The first stage would be the miners themselves in blasting the ore in a vein.

Station – The opening of the shaft at any given level underground. The main stations were rooms blasted out of the rock next to the shaft, one every 200 vertical feet. They were supported with timber, and accessed the tunnels away from the shaft. In the Granite Mountain they were approximately fourteen feet high, twenty feet in width, extended thirty or more feet back from the shaft, with excavated "pockets" into which ore was dumped from the rail cars, from which it was fed into a skip in the shaft. The floor of the station was covered with iron turnsheets, which allowed empty one-ton rail cars to be turned and put back on the rails and taken back by the motor.

Station tenders – Men assigned to specific stations who aid in loading and unloading, or directing traffic and hoisting at a particular level.

Stringer – Thin veins of ore (see also **Horsetail**).

Stope – Any excavation made in a mine to remove ore. Usually it is extended upward from one drift on one level to a higher drift, removing the vein or ore body in between. Generally they were supported by a heavy lattice or scaffolding of timber using a square set design. Many of the veins extended for several thousand feet vertically, so the stoping would eventually empty this space of ore, and the mined-out parts were filled with waste rock.

NOTE: Stopes are referred to by level and number, and sometimes with a letter addition. The 2439C for example, where Manus Duggan tried to climb up, is on the 2400 level, drift number 39 with "C" designating the switch. In the Speculator, as you went north away from the shaft on the main crosscut on all the deeper levels, the A switch went into the Jessie vein drift, the B switch went into the Lynchburg and Gem drifts, the C switch went into the Croesus and Snowball vein drifts. In short drifts, the stope could have the same designation as the drift. Hence, Duggan took the 2439C raise in the 2439C drift.

Stoper – A small hammer drill used to drill upward in a stope.

Stull – A timber or post wedged in place between two walls of a stope to help support the rock, or as part of a protective support, covering, or platform.

Sump – The bottom of a shaft that is used to collect drainage water. The sump was the lowest spot and all the ground water collected there, forcing every mine to have high powered pumping stations. In the disaster, in the week the Granite Mountain pumps were out, water filled the bottom 700 feet of the mine.

Sun-room – A floor in a stope that sticks out into previously excavated open space. The name is both descriptive and a mining joke, like a room in a house that has windows and sticks out for a view outside.

Square set timbering – A style of creating a timber frame, with the ends cut in a standard four-sided way that nestled together tightly. The same sized timbers were used nearly everywhere, so were standardized. It was invented by the German mining engineer Philipp Deidesheimer in the 1860s when he was asked to devise a secure method of stoping that could be used in the dangerously soft and unconsolidated silver ore deposits of the Comstock Lode in Nevada. This support system became universally used in hard rock mining.

Switch – The rail switches that lead from a crosscut into different major drifts, each associated with a specific major ore vein. In the Speculator, going north from the shaft, there were the A, B , C, and D switches, which referred to the Jessie, Lynchburg-Gem-Croesus, and Snowball veins. Drifts may also split, with switches at each junction.

Timber – Refers to any underground wooden supports, used in the shaft, the drifts, and crosscuts, and up in the stopes. Usually eight inch-by-eight inch square-cut timbers are used, but it can be any combination of sizes. In those days most timber was round with only the ends framed.

Timbers were used rather than iron or steel, because the ground water was highly acidic, due to the sulfide ores. Iron or steel would quickly rust and could not be used except in dry places. Timbers also were "pickled" in an arsenic bath to prevent rotting.

Timbering – Setting up or constructing timber supports in mine workings to protect men from falling rock

Timbermen – Men whose job was specifically to construct supports for main passageways and shafts.

Timber set – A specific frame made of eight-inch thick or larger timbers used to support the top, sides, and floors of stopes, passageways, or shafts, forming an interlocking frame six feet from set to set.

Trip (of ore) – A train of loaded mine cars.

Trolley box – A wooden frame nailed into the ceiling of the drifts to protect men from the electrified trolley wire. Men died from being electrocuted when they accidently touched the wire with a bar or shovel they were carrying over their shoulders.

Upcast shaft – A shaft through which air leaves the mine.

Vein – mineral ore deposited in a fissure, in Butte this was quartz and sulfide ores within walls of granite. Veins could be from six inches to 40 feet wide and run irregularly to continuously for thousands of feet. For example, the Edith May vein extended at least 3000 vertical feet into the earth, broken in places by faults. The Jessie vein was between 15 and 40 feet wide containing copper ore from the 1000 foot level to the 1800 foot level (this section was mined by the North Butte company from 1905 to 1911) and became much thinner below this.

Ventilation door – A wooden or iron door that can be open or closed to regulate air flow. Sometimes pressure differences are so great that it is almost impossible to open a door. Ventilation was just becoming a science by 1917, and the North Butte company was among the pioneers. In addition to changes in air pressure, men below the 3000 level worked with rock temperatures of 100-120 degrees and 95 to 98% humidity, while in winter the air could be minus 35 at the surface, with 10% humidity. All of these factors greatly affect air flow in a mine.

Ventilation fan – Large fans from 5 to 100 horsepower used to force air through mine workings, or up or down shafts to keep air fresh underground. These fans were just beginning to be used by 1917, and the North Butte Company was in the forefront of using them to improve ventilation throughout the mine, and especially deep in the working stopes and drifts.

Winze – Internal shafts that were driven down to explore the continuity of the vein below the lowest active mining level. As mining progressed in the area, they might become a raise.

Workings – Any of the tunnels, drifts, crosscuts, manways, raises, chutes, etc., underground in the mine.

Widow-maker – A stoper drill that used a hammering action to drill upward so the cuttings would fall out of the hole. Drilling required the miner to stand close and rotate the entire drill to keep the bit cutting a round hole. All the dust fell into his breathing area. The quartz (silica) in the rock lodged in the lungs, eventually reducing their capacity and killing the miner slowly, creating a widow. A miner was often a gasping old man by his early forties.